FEELING GOOD MATTERS
The Yoga of Mind, Medicine, and Healing

FEELING
GOOD
MATTERS

The Yoga of Mind, Medicine, and Healing

Susan Taylor, PhD

Center for Meditation Science

Center for Meditation Science
99 Grimms Road
Honesdale, Pennsylvania 18431
www.drsusantaylor.com

Content and Production Editor: Marlene Switzer (Write To Know)
Conceptual Development: Izabela Kubinska (kubinskaizabela@gmail.com)
Logo Design: Dagmara Czarnota (www.DagmaraCzarnota.com)
Illustrations: Samrat Chakraborty (www.samrats-artgallery.com)
Cover & Interior Design: Joan Greenblatt (www.CenterPointeMedia.com)
Back Cover Photo: Karl Blaser (www.KarlBlaserPhotography.com)

ISBN: 978-0-9768291-1-9
Library of Congress Cataloging-in-Publication Data: 2015906603

"A human being is an island of excellence. We are born to excel. We are surrounded—from every direction in every respect—by the intrinsic power and creativity of the divine. Our core is Pure Consciousness; luminosity is our essential nature. Our most distinctive attribute is our ability to know our own essence— our own intrinsic divinity.

Life is a priceless gift, for life endows us with everything we need to experience our grandeur. Discovering the intrinsic divinity at our core is the highest achievement; dying without experiencing it is the greatest loss."

—PANDIT RAJMANI TIGUNAIT, PHD
THE SECRET OF THE YOGA SUTRA

Table of Contents

Feeling Good Matters

Acknowledgments

The publication of *Feeling Good Matters: The Yoga of Mind, Medicine, and Healing* would not have occurred without the people who shared their unique talents and experiences with me. Their selfless encouragement through everything, from the book's concept to its content development, guided and fueled the long creative process.

My deepest gratitude to Joan Greenblatt, a gifted and dedicated graphic design mentor, whose expertise and guidance helped to transform this manuscript into an effective guide. Without her, this book would not exist in its present form.

To Marlene Switzer, a brilliant journalist, editor, and sincere friend and human being who spent endless months reading and re-reading the content to polish it for readership.

To my scientific consultants and friends, Phil O'Neil and Dr. Nick Hall, for their review and critique.

A special thanks to George and Lynn Goldstone for their endless support in all of my projects. They keep my vision alive on the Web with technical support, consulting, and media production.

To dear and trusted friends Jamie and Phil Jensen, Nancy Hess, Tom Kenison, and Kathleen Lubanski, for their continual discussions and review of the manuscript; to Elaine Kay for her consulting and advice on the title, *Feeling Good Matters;* and Matthew Greenblatt for his guidance on how to make this book available to a more mainstream readership.

Thanks to the www.DrSusanTaylor.com community of Meditation Specialists and the students and seminar attendees who support my vision to make the world a better place.

To the residents and faculty of the Himalayan Institute, for their authentic training and their generosity in providing a stage for my seminars and retreats in a holistic, healing environment.

I also wish to acknowledge the one who mentored and nourished every step of my life, the one who has awakened me from a deep sleep so I can experience how great it is to be a human being—for without the guidance and endless nurturing, I would have little to say.

And for BJ, wherever you are now … I thank you for giving me life!

INTRODUCTION

The Yoga of Mind, Medicine, and Healing

"Yoga is experiential science. The secret of yoga lies in practice; the success in practice is dependent on the quality of your mind … the more calm, tranquil and inwardly turned the mind, the easier it is for you to experience the essence of yoga."
—PANDIT RAJMANI TIGUNAIT, PHD

Life involves an infinitely complex interrelation of forces, so if we seek to make sense of it, we must examine the whole picture. Our addiction to quick fixes leads us to address individual aspects of our lives when seeking the source of problems, but comprehending the complete anatomy of our being is the only way to produce a sustainable solution.

Health is a dynamic state that includes total well-being, not merely a lack of symptoms. If we expect to "feel good," we must restore our vitality, and that flows from knowing all dimensions of ourselves in order to integrate their biochemical, physiological, and psychological aspects. We learn to focus and calm our mind. We use the food we feed our mind and body as our medicine. And we harness our innate healing force to transform our current state of being.

What we discover from working with our inner instrument, called *mind*, will far exceed what Western World research models offer. We know that how we *perceive* affects how we *feel*, which not only changes things in the moment, but also leaves behind a vibrational footprint. And that creates the threads of the fabric that makes up our brain, body, and experience.

There are no instruments to measure the subtlety of how our mind works, nor how it can be used to heal us and our planet. However, when we're aware of our body—the physical layer of mind—we can gain access to the intricacies of what makes us *who* and *what* we are. Our body becomes the barometer for feedback since it is more difficult to directly gain access to the workings of the mind through thinking. For example, the right combinations of foods, herbs, and sensory impressions constitute healing medicine that can make us "dance." When our dance is fluid and fun, that's when we feel good.

By this process, we become the scientists and conduct the experiment called life. We must understand the whole mind-body complex as one, which in turn serves as a tool for us to become aware of who we are. It is the awareness of our experiences that makes us truly human.

As we journey into our own being, the light of awareness will begin to shine through the many layers of our existence. Once we get a glimpse of this experience—or perhaps we've already witnessed it—we can build momentum on the path toward fulfilling our life's purpose. Healing will no longer be a mystery.

Through this book's lessons, we will learn to question current psychiatric diagnoses regarding anxiety and depression; we will become versed in the anatomy of brain and mind, our digestion, and its relation to the quality of our thoughts and emotions; and, finally, we will acquire the ability to use meditation to investigate the root causes of our dissatisfaction.

"Take up one idea. Make that one idea your life—
think of it, dream of it, live on that idea. Let the
brain, muscles, nerves, every part of your body, be full
of that idea, and just leave every other idea alone.
This is the way to success."
—SWAMI VIVEKANANDA

The Yoga of Mind, Medicine, and Healing is more than a series of lessons with practices. Its lessons form a passageway that each person must navigate to discover the source of the innate power of intelligence—the healing force. Treading this path requires determination, focus and practice, but the journey culminates in a rebalanced body, mind, and soul. It's also a means to experience the vitality and pure joy that is our birthright.

The lessons presented in this book are intended to introduce us to our Self, where our innate power to heal dwells. Armed with knowledge about our Self, we can learn to trust the personal data we acquire. *We can step into the light of freedom and live our purpose in life.* It will require patience and practice, and this can be learned.

The roots of disease are somewhere other than where we've been looking. Embedded deep within our unconscious mind, they reveal themselves only through our personal perseverance and determination—practice. Once again, we must be patient, as there is no time element to this process. It is life—a continuum, a journey.

We should expect to be amazed; we'll enjoy our exploration. And I know *we absolutely can do this.*

This book is based on the experiences encountered on my path of practice. I have structured each lesson in such a way that, if followed, it will help in restoring the vitality and focus needed to find and fulfill each person's life purpose. I have identified five principles of healing that are incorporated in the lessons throughout the book, practices that work for me on a daily basis. We must maintain ways to sustain a focused and calm mind if we want to reach our destiny. This new medicine includes forming and nurturing healthy relationships, eating nourishing foods, cultivating positive thoughts and feelings, and caring for others. When we do for others, we not only serve another human being but actually serve our higher Self and feed good vibrations to our environment.

Each of the book's 12 lessons has three sections: a theme, path of practice, and review. The theme section discusses scientific matters; the path of practice section gives us a journal activity designed to record our inner feelings and thoughts on specific subjects, followed by core practices to support the given topic. The review section offers a summary of the facts and obstacles that we need to address to feel good.

The lessons—topics, journal writing, core practices, and review—are designed to support us on our path toward healing. The work can actually reprogram our mental GPS to keep us on course. The core practices advance from basic to the more complex. The techniques described in each exercise are organized in prepared sequences for a more skilled practice. As much as these are definitive, there is also a degree of flexibility to customize one's own routine.

Ultimately, *The Yoga of Mind, Medicine, and Healing* is a book that can guide us in restoring our life force, our vitality and, with it, self-confidence, optimism, and the joy of living. The teachings spread over the lessons are based on yoga science combined with and supported by the most recent discoveries in mainstream science. We learn how to improve the quality of our life, regardless of our financial and professional status, by establishing some healthy habits through much-tried and tested practices.

Each lesson builds on the next to form a healing circle, always starting and finishing with the Self. The result will be an informed and changed Self—one who is self-aware, not self-conscious. We'll be equipped with tools to relax when tense and will learn ways to nourish ourselves properly when depleted.

This might seem like a tall order, but everything is possible with practice and the willingness to discover who we really are. Such is what the lessons have to offer: my guidance and experience on how to self-heal; followed by my own path of practice based on yoga asanas, breathing, relaxation, body-mind diet, and meditation.

We start healing by recognizing a fundamental principle that the quality of our thoughts depends on what we feed our mind.

THE PREMISE IS ILLUSTRATED BY THIS
NATIVE AMERICAN STORY.

An elder Cherokee was teaching
her grandchildren about life.
She told them:

"A fight is going on inside me. It is a terrible fight and it is between two wolves. One wolf represents fear, anger, hatred, envy, sorrow, regret, greed, arrogance, self-pity, guilt, resentment, inferiority, lies, false pride, superiority and ego. The other stands for joy, peace, love, hope, sharing, serenity, humility, kindness, benevolence, friendship, empathy, generosity, truth, compassion and faith. This same fight is going on inside of you, and inside every other person, too."

They thought about it for a minute,
and then one child asked his grandmother:
"Which wolf will win?"

The elder Cherokee replied:
"The one you feed."

"You need to understand yourself on all levels. You don't need much external information; you already have true knowledge within. You need to learn how to apply the knowledge that you have."

—SWAMI RAMA

LESSON 1

It's a Matter of Knowing Who You Are

W ho we are is a composite of what others tell us and, with that in mind, what we think about ourselves. This lesson begins our journey to discover who we truly are by becoming fully aware of what shapes us physically and mentally. Now we begin to peel back the layers that prevent us from *discovering* ourselves.

LEARN TO READ THE LABEL

"Who goes there, friend or foe?" Our need to categorize others may have its origin in primal survival measures, but the human condition now reflects the consequences of indiscriminate labeling. I'm not referring to something repugnant, like placing people in castes or practicing bigotry. Most labels are subtle, rendered without malice, but they contribute to our concept of our place in life. Favorable labels buoy us and make us feel good about ourselves, whether or not we earned the praise. Those unfortunate people burdened by negative labels can find life more difficult to navigate.

"Johnny is a good boy." "Sheryl is not a happy child." "Sally is smart." "Mikie won't pay attention." The subliminal messages delivered by such labels define the template for who we think we are and believe we could be, as well as who we really are and can expect to be.

Living our lives, we unwittingly accumulate an infinite list of tags associated with our conscious behavior, intrinsic qualities, and perceived potential. None carries the weight of a diagnosis that explains why we just don't feel good. When we seek professional assistance to sort out symptoms we suffer, we're apt to receive another label, owing to the prevailing tendency to diagnose and prescribe instead of uncovering the root cause of those symptoms. We're sad, fatigued, distracted, overwhelmed ... feelings that can be appropriate short-term responses but can also render us incapable of functioning in the world.

Is it a mood disorder, such as depression or anxiety? With medication and therapy, we can expect to feel better, but will we thereafter identify with the diagnosis, perceiving symptoms consistent with it? Can we ever experience fatigue or distraction as pertinent responses to life without attributing those "symptoms" to our disease label? I believe we first must examine our self-perception in order to discern whether our symptoms could be healed through dietary support, homeopathy, breathing practices, and meditation.

I always caution students, "Put your labels on a jar. If you hold onto them, you'll own them through identification." This isn't to suggest that diagnostic categories have no relevance, but I believe we must examine symptoms of the diagnosis without permanently labeling ourselves. What we tell ourselves through our mind chatter can crystallize into matter, such as a condition in the body.

This was demonstrated by one of my students who complained of stress burnout. Robert was an executive recruiter who had to leave his job after suffering a breakdown. The warning signs were present, if only he had paid attention. Working more than 75 hours a week over nine months, Robert's body generated messages that he was pushing too hard.

"Always remember that you are absolutely unique.
Just like everyone else."
—MARGARET MEAD

He came to one of our retreats after a medical evaluation that found he had anxiety and depression, for which he was prescribed medication. During the evening class, when I asked students to share their reasons for participating, Robert said he was there on the suggestion of a former co-worker and hoped the class would help him find ways to deal with his troubling conditions.

He spoke with obvious pain, admitting he feared what could be "wrong with him." I asked him to describe his symptoms, to which he replied, "…anxiety and deep remorse," then added that he was concerned about his future. His doctors had explained that "these things happen."

"It just happened to show up at this time in my life," Robert said.

Although he lacked specific knowledge about his health, Robert believed there were no other solutions. Ironically, he had established a situation for his body and mind in which his symptoms took up residence and reinforced the diagnosis of a permanent problem. His association with the label caused Robert's body—with its innate intelligence—to manufacture the biochemical reactions that would support what the mind was telling it.

When you label something and identify with it, thinking *"I have depression"* or *"I have anxiety,"* you give it a home, a place to take hold and reside. Seeing yourself as "a person with a condition" and being unaware of what you're feeding your mind actually allows the condition to become part of the makeup of your entire being. Our body mirrors our mind. There is no separation.

In other words, what we think and associate with is what the intelligence of our body creates for us. So become aware of the quality of your messages to yourself. Labels confine us. They limit our freedom by placing boundaries around all possibilities.

There is a way out of this conundrum. Become aware, first and foremost. Acknowledge the symptoms as nothing more than that. To accomplish this, we use our body as feedback, because it's difficult to reach the mind to work with it intellectually.

This is the premise I've adopted for myself and those who have worked with me to overcome stress-related mental health issues:

Keep the labels on jars. You're feeling symptoms, nothing more. They can be treated through lifestyle changes in diet and nutrition, movement and exercise, and with meditation that addresses how you think.

A "labeled condition" can be stubborn. Change your lifestyle, but continue to think, *"I am depressed," "I am anxious,"* and you won't override what the mind is feeding the cellular mechanisms in the body and the brain. When we practice mindfulness, then bring it into focus, we can become aware of our identity. That's the first step in uncovering the root cause of our illnesses so we can develop a more holistic and sustainable plan for living.

WE NEED TO MIND OUR BODIES

Let's turn to the yoga science model of who we really are. Remaining in a state of homeostasis, or balance, is when we feel and function best, but we can experience periods of imbalance. For example, during those episodes of anger, agitation, or jealousy—no matter how brief—every person actually has a "mental problem." These mental issues are a condition of being human and shouldn't be a source of shame. Consider the pervasive negative connotation of mental illness in contrast to diabetes, renal failure, or heart disease. Ask yourself why this paradox exists when many physical maladies are rooted in the mind.

As an illustration of this question, I'm reminded of Lisa, a client who suffered from anxiety related to adrenal burnout. The hospital that employed her took advantage of Lisa's dedication and chronically overworked her. In our initial meeting, Lisa told me that her supervisor had spoken candidly about having colitis, but after Lisa suffered a "mental breakdown" and sought help, this supervisor became condescending toward her. The irony here was that Lisa's supervisor had unresolved mental issues that manifested in her bowel, whereas Lisa actually recognized that her anxiety was the precursor of physical disease. Lisa's experience demonstrates how society stigmatizes mental issues and fails to acknowledge that diseases of the body can result from mental disturbance.

CONCENTRATE ON UNCONSCIOUS AWARENESS

Our body is the object of our rapt attention, owing to its constant material presence, but our mind is another aspect of our being that receives far less respect. We concentrate on training our relatively small conscious mind through formal education. In contrast, the unconscious mind is a vast reservoir into which we continually pour all the things we do, including memories and impressions of the past and thoughts of the future. Anything we have sensed, imagined, or thought resides in the storehouse of the unconscious mind.

We'll see later in this book that meditation—bringing mindfulness into focus—helps train this aspect of the mind so we aren't allured to go west when we're heading east. The senses are employed by the mind for our interaction with the outside world. They're the source of our pleasure and pain. If we learn to work with the sensory mind and avoid feeding into its likes and dislikes, we can be happy and content with our life experiences.

Remaining calm, no matter what, is important to a healthy mind. Being calm is a state in which we have continual awareness, and this occurs when we live in the moment. Each of our trillions of cells that make up our matter (physical-energetic matrix) has its individual center of awareness. When we translate this in scientific terms, our brain (body included) consists of trillions of cells, and those trillions of cells comprise the center of awareness. Each of these cells has its own intelligence, with the ability to make choices about what is needed for our organism to sustain itself in a "good" space.

It's that aspect of our being that knows how to provide nutrients for the body and protect us from harmful bacteria and viruses. It's the intelligence that causes egg and sperm to unite to create a human being.

Before we can begin to work on changing ourselves, we must identify our starting point. Recognizing and accepting what habits we possess is that first step. Everyone wants to be better than he or she is—"better" having different meaning for each of us. So we skip steps and try to get to the front of the line. We struggle so hard to get there, only to discover we've missed out on some of the necessary skills, and we fall to the back of the line again.

See how this supports that scenario: A student in one of my classes told me that the most exhilarating time of her life was when she stopped trying to know everything and be perfect. Ellen spent years in academia, and since the beginning of her PhD training in molecular biology, she had become accustomed to being put on the spot. She created such a groove in her mind that she went into "panic mode" when preparing for a meeting. The following *thoughts* were Ellen's habitual pattern: "What if I didn't know? Would I still graduate?" The mind saw danger and created a stress response.

In primordial times, a human would be distressed by the possibility of being killed and eaten. Today, we respond to the loss of our false identity, such as our job title, at the same threat level. We're still reacting to the fearful thought, *"What will happen to me?"*

Here's why the two responses to perceived mortal threats have very different effects on the body. You, the cave dweller, run like the wind when the hungry sabre-tooth tiger approaches. Neurochemicals released by your fear-flight response fuel your survival run. You, the insurance company customer service rep, discover your job has been eliminated and an automated system will replace you. The news causes you to experience the same type of reaction as the cave dweller. Your body releases powerful neurochemicals to fuel your escape, but you don't run.

These chemicals damage body tissues and can create new brain responses to perceived threats. Over many years, this pathway becomes one's way of responding without realizing it's against the wisdom of the body and mind.

We all want to be useful and recognized, to have satisfying careers, to accomplish more than possible because standards are constantly being raised. We're feeling the effect of a global economic system that rewards growth but not sustainability. Is it any wonder that we behave in ways that don't consider long-term health and well-being?

COMMITTING CRIMES AGAINST WISDOM

Let's look at how we get out of balance, since this seems to be at the root of our not feeling good. Our organism (here meaning "our body-brain-mind complex") knows what it needs and doesn't need. It has an innate intelligence like nature herself.

We're unlike fellow animals whose lives are in tune with a metabolic clock set by nature. They instinctively know what and when to eat, how to rest, when to throw up their food. Their survival quite literally is at stake.

All animals have minds that operate under the forces of nature, but our minds have a function that can override nature. We're able to make decisions that counter nature's intelligence, which can present a problem if we don't have the awareness—the clarity—to know what's good and not so good for us.

Here's an example of how we experience this: It's late at night when Linda suddenly craves ice cream. She knows it will affect her sleep and digestion, as well as subvert her efforts to lose weight, but to avoid dealing with a troublesome emotional situation, Linda rationalizes that a little bit of ice cream, just this once, will be okay. With each spoonful, she justifies her choice by saying she had a hard day and deserves a treat. *I'll begin a diet tomorrow,* Linda thinks.

Unfortunately, the effect of this action won't be limited to the bowl of ice cream that satisfied the late-night craving. Linda feels a twinge of guilt but refuses to acknowledge it, so when the sweet craving returns the next evening (she still has that pesky emotional quandary), she satisfies it with cookies. Thus begins a nighttime snack habit. Linda believes consuming anything sweet will counteract her not feeling so sweet. Although she knows her body will suffer, her emotional mind trumps the intelligence. "Just this once" becomes "more than once," and a habit is born. This new habit becomes Linda's reality, and she totally forgets what the innate intelligence of her body whispered to her several months earlier.

From an Ayurvedic perspective, when we start to regard something as reality that isn't the intelligence of our consciousness, we commit a *"crime against wisdom."* We grasp for something externally or internally to ultimately feel good, ignoring its effect on our mind's health.

Product marketers are masterful at allurement. Clever advertisements convince us to eat their pizza because it tastes so good. We pop two antacids afterward. We're promised ways to feel better, but deep inside we know there's no shortcut. Over time, the allurement becomes a habit and that's our new reality.

This is when our GPS (Global Positioning System) misreads the map. We begin to lose our focus and ability to perceive things accurately, and we justify our decisions rather than listen to what we know is right and wrong for us. Our mind wants it, so justification is there. Our innate intelligence has lost perspective, and now we live with this new habit that we deem our reality, although it causes ill health. We know the truth deep within ourselves, but the part of the mind making these decisions that are based on allurement is now in charge. It places a veil over the light of intelligence—inner awareness—that dwells within us.

When we lose receptivity to our innate intelligence, problems begin to surface in our body and mind. I offered a simple example of unwise eating, but we can delve even deeper to recognize this behavior in any repeated behavior that doesn't serve our higher Self. The amount of time and ways we've been traveling contrary to our innate intelligence will determine how long it will take us to return to feeling good. We must develop a strategy to return to our center. It's absolutely within our reach. We just need to recognize the patterns and learn to navigate our being.

The journey is life. If it's not one thing, it's another. It's all okay because we have the tools as a human being to override the negative programming and reshape our life. Restoring balance depends on our ability to stay calm and to focus. If we're calm and focused, the change can happen instantaneously. We only must sustain it in the most stressful situations, when things aren't going our way.

We can be set free if we accept the reality of our circumstance, without judgment. We can stop the stress cycle by assessing what's useful and what's not. We understand the motive behind our actions. We witness our reactions to circumstances.

This concept can be applied to every facet of life but requires that we be aware. With our new level of awareness we can begin to address our specific habits and their influence on our health, which is the subject of our next lesson.

Review

TRUTH
The labels we create form our habits and become our reality.

OBSTACLE
We confine our Self to a label.

EXIT STRATEGY
Let go of labels and thoroughly examine symptoms.

FACTS

- ❖ Our body mirrors what our mind is reflecting.

- ❖ Our physical conditions are rooted in the mind.

- ❖ We commit *"crimes against wisdom"* when ignoring our intelligence.

- ❖ We can be set free when we accept who we are.

Path *of* Practice

The only way that we can truly understand and know who we are is acquired through the experience. This experience is gained not from knowing the path, but walking the path of practice. Though the path has its peaks and valleys, we must travel on if we are going to reach our destination where fulfillment resides.

Travel on and be the
light for others.

♋ JOURNAL WRITING ♋

Journal writing has many purposes. You may want to document your progress in meditation; it can be an activity to set goals, or be used as a private means of expressing your feelings and ideas. The process of keeping a journal helps you learn more about yourself. Journaling can give you the perspective of where you are emotionally as well as physically on a particular day.

Historically, journals have been used to provide insight into a day in the life, behind the scenes, comings and goings of artists, writers, scientists, travelers, and anyone else who cared to keep one. Writing is a powerful tool for giving clarity, directing focus, and "reprogramming" the mind.

Technique:

1. Buy a journal or notebook of a convenient size and shape. Make sure it's large enough to write in comfortably but small enough to take with you. Preferably choose one without lines. They keep you within a boundary, but without lines you're free to create what you like. You can order one from www.drsusantaylor.com or find your own.

2. Choose a pen with permanent ink, especially if you're writing a journal for your posterity. Some inks will fade with time.

3. Determine a regular schedule for writing. As with any habit, you should write at approximately the same time each day.

4. Find a quiet place where you won't be interrupted or allured away.

5. Remember the purpose of your journal before you write. Add sketches, quotes, and personal experiences, as appropriate. Each lesson in this book will have a theme for your journaling to guide you in your self-inquiry on the way to healing. Make it a point to keep with the basic form.

6. Start writing. Keep an open perspective and awareness. You can follow the suggestions or create your own objectives.

JOURNAL ACTIVITY

Purpose:

To be made aware of who you are by knowing how you label your likes and dislikes, what's good and what's bad. Discover how you see yourself through what you identify with and continue to use your breath to remain aware in the moment.

Technique:

1. Observe how you react to comments about you. Do you feel pride when praised or do you try to discredit your achievement? Do you think, *"Oh, she's just trying to be polite"* or *"He just wants something in exchange"*?

2. How do you react to constructive feedback? Does it make you depressed or do you think, *"Next time I'll do better"*? How do you react to unjustified feedback? Do you get angry? Do you feel low or become defensive? Do you begin to resent the person who gave feedback or labeled you?

3. Record your likes and dislikes for one week. In addition, write something about how you see yourself and how you want others to see you. You might use two paragraphs to separate *your* view from your perception of how *others* view you.

Core Practices

We must establish a firm and stable foundation to support our journey into awareness. Firmness and stability of our seat translates to our psychological and emotional well-being.

We'll begin with some variations on the seated posture as an alternative to a chair. Once the seat is established, it can be used for breathing and meditation practices.

The benefit of all these practices developed from yoga asana is to establish a meditation seat.

Easy Pose (Sukhasana)

Purpose:

To establish a steady and firm seat/posture for practices.

Technique:

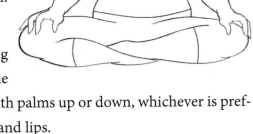

1. Sit with the head, neck, and spine aligned. Fold the legs—left leg under the right thigh—in a comfortable position. Sit upright.

2. Relax the arms along your side and place the hands on the thighs with palms up or down, whichever is preferable. Close the eyes and lips.

Props:

Use folded blankets or a meditation cushion under the buttocks to elevate the pelvis so it's higher than the knees. You may want to put cushions or rolled blankets under the knees to keep them supported if they're not touching the floor.

Thunderbolt Pose (Vajrasana)

Purpose:

To establish a steady and firm seat for practices.

Technique:

1. Kneel on a thick blanket or zabuton (large square cushion used for meditation). Allow the knees to be slightly apart with big toes touching.

2. With the arms alongside, allow the buttocks to slowly lower onto the heels. Use the hands to support the body while lowering. Hold the head, neck, and trunk aligned.

3. Allow the hands to rest on the thighs. Relax the entire body. Close the eyes and the lips.

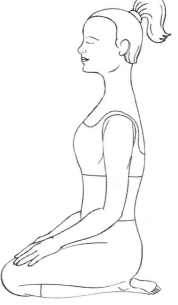

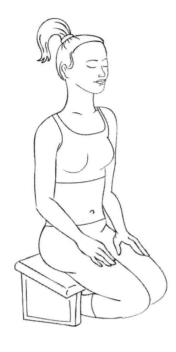

Vajrasana with Zazen Bench

You can use a meditation bench also, called a *zazen bench,* instead of being directly on the floor. You can roll a yoga blanket and straddle it if the knees and ankles aren't able to withstand the pressure of the weight of the body. Many students use this technique.

Note: *This practice can be uncomfortable and even painful for the knees and ankles. It shouldn't be practiced if there is pain.*

So Ham Breathing ("I am that pure awareness")

The core practice of So Ham (pronounced "so-hum") breathing will help make you aware of who you are. Over time, this will serve as an anchor for the mind. It will help you keep the mind on track to avoid falling prey to suggestions of who you are as perceived by others.

Purpose:

A technique to calm and focus the mind.

Technique:

1. Sit in one of the meditative postures listed above. If this isn't comfortable, sit on a chair with the head, neck, and trunk aligned, with the feet flat on the floor. If you need a cushion under the buttocks to raise the hips so they're higher than the knees, do so.

2. Close the eyes and bring your awareness to the breath. Inhale and exhale, and allow each breath to flow smoothly and evenly, without jerks or pauses.

3. Focus on the breath as if, on inhalation, it travels from the base of the spine to the top of the head and, on an exhalation, it travels from the top of the head to the base of the spine. Do this for a few breaths.

4. On the next inhalation, follow the breath while mentally hearing the sound "so" as you travel up the front of the spinal column to the top of the head. On exhalation, mentally hear the sound "hum" as you travel from the top of the head down the back of the spine.

5. Do this mental repetition "so" on the inhalation and "hum" on the exhalation for as long as you like. Doing this daily for 40 days, you will see tremendous benefits to your health.

Note: *There are more advanced versions of this practice, but I have found this version to be of great benefit.*

"The state of ill health is a moment-to-moment happening. Healing is moment-to-moment balance, bringing awareness to our thoughts, feelings and emotions and how we respond."

—VASANT LAD
AYURVEDIC PHYSICIAN

LESSON 2

It's a Matter of Habit

Everyone has habits—both good and troublesome—some obvious, others unrecognized. Whether or not we acknowledge their existence, we can't deny the role of habits in the way we interact with and live in our world. Habitual attitudes, actions, and thoughts constitute our individuality; they're manifested in every choice we make.

In this lesson, we'll learn how to identify our habits. Once they're uncovered, we can escape their effect and be free to create new habits that sustain the energy to fulfill our life purpose.

PUT OUR SELVES ON SOLID FOOTING

Our mind, body, and spirit foundation is supported when we're focused and calm. That's when we can be vital and feel good. The very essence of our being—vital energy—is the life force that courses through everything. Although age diminishes the life force, our daily habits determine how we'll fare in that inevitable process. For the lessons that follow, we'll reinforce our foundation with habits that keep us focused on nourishing our energy field and give us the vitality necessary to achieve our life's purpose.

Vital energy circulates throughout our physical-psychological matrix. It comes from the cultivation of our inner fire—the heat that transforms our foods into nutrients and our will into action. How we tend to this fire through our physical and mental habits determines the quality of our life energy. With solid practices in the areas of nutrition, breathing, movement, and meditation, we manage this inner fire and sustain a healthy and vital life with access to our source of healing.

Some 30 years of experience studying yoga science, Ayurvedic, and Traditional Chinese Medicine has demonstrated to me the power of working with the mind. We can prevail once we learn to deal with the fundamental principles of collecting, containing, and circulating our energy field. It's possible to restore our body and mind complex on a regular basis *from within* by cultivating habits that nourish and support our being. We only have to recognize and walk the pathway to feeling good.

To prepare for the journey, we need a solid foundation. We first address the physical body since it's the most practical and accessible. We do this by assessing its strengths and weaknesses. We build our diet, breathing, and movement practices to optimize digestion, nerve transmission, respiration, and resilience.

On a psychological level, we need to become aware of our fears and self-doubts, and their sources, so we can move forward with complete confidence and trust. On a spiritual level, we must recognize that we are the architects of our own life. It is only through living our life's purpose that we find contentment, joy, and fulfillment.

Even with the best intentions to change our lifestyle, we can tire within days and revert to old habits that are rooted in our likes and dislikes. This will occur repeatedly if we've failed to create a firm foundation. Think of what we would do if we were to discover a huge crack in our home's cellar just before undertaking a kitchen remodeling project. There would be no question that the basement should be made sound before proceeding.

That example mirrors how we prepare for our journey. We create a foundation that will sustain us at our summit: a stable body, balanced breathing, positive emotions, and a calm and focused mind. Throughout our lessons in this book, all practices will bear out this formula.

HOW WE LIVE SUPPORTS HOW WE FEEL

There are obvious benefits to living in a way that is conducive to feeling good. We merely have to develop daily habits that align with those practices that support a healthy and vital body and mind.

That premise is exemplified in weekend retreats that offer people a refuge from stress. Participants expect to feel good. They're helped to identify and confront what bothers them. It's worth the time and effort, as they return with a newly acquired peace of mind. Ironically, many report losing that sense of centeredness only a few days after the retreat.

I'm continually asked why the peacefulness is fleeting. The reason is simple: The habits practiced at the retreat center are different from those at home. At the retreat center, participants get out of bed early; meals are freshly prepared; yoga and meditation sessions are offered; there are no TVs, Internet, or mobile devices. In the evening, there's time for study, chanting, and meditation. The environment is set up to support stability, calmness, and nourishment. The foundation is reinforced.

But old habits trump those new ones practiced at the retreat. Even with the best intentions, many people revert to waking late, snacking after dinner, tuning in to TV, or surfing the Internet close to bedtime. The demands of their environment take their focus off change. It's a clear case of distraction.

The power of imbedded habits can prevent the newly learned retreat habits from taking hold, so I suggest a measured approach. For example, at the end of the day, skip television and the Internet, drink a cup of tea (instead of snacking), and read or do artwork before sleep. Try to wake up at home near 5:45 a.m., the time when the day began at the retreat. Still quiet and serene, it will be easier to prepare for the day ahead.

Over the course of about a month on this new schedule, most people experience immensely positive changes in their energy levels, productivity, overall mood, and creativity. By adjusting their routine—and giving new behaviors time to become habits—many find their homes beginning to mirror a retreat setting.

We know that our day-in day-out lifestyles directly affect our health and well-being. What we falsely believe is that we're at the mercy of our habits and the routines dictated by our work and family lives. A weekend workshop or one-week vacation is deemed a success if it makes us feel calm and rested, energized and fully alive. Within days (if not hours) of returning to "real" life, though, we again may be feeling fatigued, anxious, and stuck.

Many expect to change how they feel without modifying the habit patterns so engrained in their lifestyle. We must break out of that pattern or risk ending up with the same short-term positive results. The only way to change how we feel is to change what we're doing. Wouldn't you agree?

Keep in mind that our lifestyles don't have to be prisons from which we can hope to be paroled on occasion. We can learn to look at our daily activities as duties rather than chores that enslave us. This requires that we change how we think about them. We can *choose* to create supportive, nourishing habit patterns that are the norm rather than seeking respites.

For example, meditation—attending to one's mind—is the ultimate restorative "feel-good" medicine, since it addresses our mind field and trains us to transform our negative thought patterns into positive ones. A daily meditation practice produces positive results in our well-being and serves as a solid foundation along with our lifestyle choices.

When looking for any lasting change, it's vital to have a solid foundation, a container. This allows us to build and maintain momentum rather than sabotage our efforts from the get-go. Without a firm foundation, we likely won't be able to follow through on our best intentions and won't ever see results.

When we start something new and, after a few days, revert to old patterns, the cause is often a lack of fundamental support. So we must produce a foundation of habits that will sustain us in our resolve to feel good.

"Your beliefs become your thoughts,
Your thoughts become your words,
Your words become your actions,
Your actions become your habits,
Your habits become your values,
Your values become your destiny."
—MAHATMA GANDHI

CREATE A NEW GROOVE

If we're to discard how we feel and move to what we can become, we must forge new habits. It's far easier to create a new one than it is to eliminate an old one. Changing a habit has been described as a never-ending battle, but why? Think of a habit as a groove in our mind. As a child, I can recall trying to steer my bicycle through the deep, mud-hardened ruts in a dirt road. Like that road, our minds develop grooves from repeating something over and over again.

Habits are both physical and mental—how we move, walk, and

talk; what we choose to see and hear; what and how we think. They're rooted very deeply in places where we don't yet have access to knowing. Instead of trying to fill in the old groove, start a new one. With it in place, we can better recognize the harm in our old habits.

Here's a practical way to create a new habit:

 Step 1

Recognize the need to change and decide you will.

Beginning with a self-inquiry journal will make it easier to see what habits inhibited you in the past. Don't judge yourself. Simply remain CALM (Consciously Aware of Living in the Moment). When you live in the moment, you're able to distinguish those habits that help you and those that create problems for you. You're also able to have more clarity in what's bothering you and what needs to be done. This is helpful in coming up with an exit strategy.

 Step 2

Identify the habit you want to create.

Write down your goal and a means to it. If your goal is to feel good, begin by regulating your sleep/wake time. Or pick a smaller goal, like walking 1,000 steps after eating dinner—something fun. Stick to it for 40 days; I've found that people are likely to revert to their old habits in less time.

The suggested habits here aren't to be done for a specific time and then stopped. They're designed to be incorporated into your life. If you slip, start again and simply acknowledge that you lapsed. Then pause, observe, detach from any judgment, and resolve that you *want to* do it, you *can* do it, and you *will* do it. The process is known as *sankalpa* in yoga science. Keep going by starting again, and soon you'll find that you're building momentum. The new behavior will become a habit. The old groove will be abandoned.

 ### Step 3
Be systematic and realistic.

Make sure to practice the new habit at approximately the same time each day. For example, if you want to adopt daily meditation, designate an optimum time of day, one that will work for 40 days. If the activity proves problematic, refer to Step 5. When you don't have time to practice the habit, like meditation, just sit on your meditation seat for one minute before heading out the door or going to bed. By performing the act of sitting, even for one minute, you enforce new behavior and support a roadway to change. It's important to work within your capacity, not create something too difficult to enjoy and pursue.

Step 4

Be consistent and persistent.

Instilling a habit requires about 40 days, so for the first month, you must act deliberately and maintain your schedule. Habits certainly can be modified once they're adopted, but early in the process, strict adherence is important. For example, when it's inconvenient to practice the new habit, your mind will allure you by saying, "You really don't need to do this today." In fact, allurement by our senses can be so convincing that even the most resolute person will want to skip a day. Do not skip.

Consistent attention to newly formed habits is akin to stoking a fire. Left unattended, the flames diminish and expire. Miss a day or two of a new practice and risk losing the progress you've made. It's important to understand this concept from the beginning. Ask a dieter about this phenomenon. She'll tell you about her optimism at the outset but, after exceeding the diet's guidelines, it was extremely difficult to make the changes necessary to start anew.

Step 5

Be flexible.

A martial arts teacher once sent me into a tournament with the sage advice to "be bamboo." He knew that being flexible like bamboo would help me to remain standing and unbroken when pressured. The ability to change within a habit, when appropriate, can make an action more readily habit forming. If scheduling your meditation time becomes a burden, be flexible. Tension builds if you become too rigid with rules. Overtighten a guitar string and it'll break; restrict yourself too much and your good intentions could fail. Useful habits should bring joy, not only in their effect but in performing them.

"Habits are cobwebs at first, cables at last."
—CHINESE PROVERB

WE'RE HABITUAL BEINGS

Our habits in total make up our being, so it's most important that they be skillfully formatted and established. To do so, we must understand the underlying forces that brought us to where we are. And we must create an exit strategy. I say "exit" rather than "vacation" because short-term approaches yield only temporary results. These may be useful or even necessary in a crisis, but ultimately they increase weakness in both body and mind, because the magic bullet we reach for—the trip, sleeping pill, massage—is outside ourselves. True happiness and feeling good can come only from inside of us.

When we're centered in ourselves, we operate from a place of wisdom. When we're conscious of the Self, there's no room for being self-conscious. We go inside and act from a point of authenticity and power. Because it lies within, this source of strength, peace, and joy is a renewable resource. We nourish and replenish it with our actions and choices—our habits of being. Meditation, which we'll observe in later lessons, is that most powerful tool to help us travel inward.

Learning new habits or routine behaviors is associated with the brain's ability to create new synapses. Many of these synapses comprise the basal ganglia, an information processor in the forebrain. Scientists theorize that this information processor is the structure that helps support our habit formation. Dopamine—a neurotransmitter implicated in being focused and motivated, thus, feeling good—assists the basal ganglia in what's called a "reward circuitry." Main motivators are natural rewards such as food, water, sleep, sex, and self-preservation and these are the basis for many of our foundational habit patterns.[1]

Looking at the cause and effect of negative behavior on the body, we can't overlook the influence of our society in overdrive. There's not enough time in the day to get our work done or to eat in ways that truly nourish us, so we seek quick fixes through shortcuts and magic bullets. We're surrounded by proof that such hasty measures are ineffective: there's an epidemic of unhappiness, exhaustion, and disease.

In the next lesson on the breath, I'll talk more extensively about how our breathing habits have the capacity to rewire our emotional and psychological well-being.

Review

TRUTH

Our habits of focus create our reality.

OBSTACLE

Habits that do not support wellness.

EXIT STRATEGY

Adopt new habits that help fulfill our life's purpose.

FACTS

❖ The basis of feeling good is rooted in our habits.

❖ Habits begin in the mind, not in the brain.

❖ Our physical health reflects our mind & its habits.

❖ Our life course changes with adopting new habits.

Path *of* Practice

"Sun Salutations bestow upon us the good fortune of having only good thoughts, of hearing and speaking only good words, and of attaining a sound and strong body, so that we may have a long life and, one day, achieve oneness with God."

—SRI K. PATTABHI JOIS

 JOURNAL ACTIVITY

Purpose:

To become more aware of your habits and the way they influence how you feel.

Technique:

Assess your habits and how they might get in the way of your well-being. The following are sample questions to help you in your self-inquiry:

1. What is your biggest concern about your health or your life?

2. Do you have purpose in your life? A clearly defined goal as to what you want to accomplish?

3. What habits do you have that might not support the strength and stamina that you need to live your life's full potential?

4. Do you find yourself wanting to do something but don't have the willpower or strength to do it? If so, what is supporting your habit and how is the habit that you have enabling you to stay stuck?

Make a list with two columns. On one side, put the habits that support strength and stamina; on the other, put the habits that deplete your vital essence.

Core Practice

"Every day we are born again,
what we do today is what matters most."
—BUDDHA

The **Sun Salutation** *(Surya Namaskara)* is one of the most complete practices of hatha yoga. The sequence of twelve physical movements correspond to the signs of the zodiac. These movements and asanas (postures) serve as a warm-up or an entire practice to establish a firm foundation for both meditation and its practices. With a few cycles of the sun salutation, you not only energize and balance the entire nervous system, but you activate your digestive fire and enhance your mood.

Purpose:

To establish a systematic foundation of movement to balance the entire nervous system and synchronize breath with movement.

Technique:

1. Start by bringing the feet together or slightly apart with your weight evenly distributed over both feet. Close the eyes or leave partially open. Place the palms together in front of the chest.

*Step 1
Prayer
Pose*

Mentally acknowledge the sun as a source of all life. Relax and bring the entire body into your awareness. Breathe normally.

2. Inhale, raise and stretch both arms overhead with palms facing upward or facing each other. Keep the arms separated shoulder distance apart and reach back slightly. Be aware of the slight arch in the upper neck region and throat area.

Step 2 Overhead Stretch

3. Begin exhaling and bend forward into

Step 3 Forward Bend

a standing forward bend. If you have tight hamstrings, keep the knees bent. Draw the navel toward the spine as you exhale completely, letting the hands reach the floor. Focus your attention at the abdominal region. *If the fingertips reach only to the thighs or knees, don't worry. Over time, you will become more flexible.* Keep the legs and feet fully engaged.

4. Inhale, extend the left foot back as far as you can and come into the lunge position. Keep the front knee directly over the ankle and the back leg firm. You may let the back shin rest on the floor or lift up on the toes into a raised lunge. Focus your attention at the eyebrow area.

Step 3 Lunge

5. Exhale, extend the right foot back to meet the left foot, straightening the legs. Take the upper body forward so the shoulders are directly over the wrists; let the hips come down at the same time. With the solar plexus area strong, settle into the plank position and hold a moment or two. Inhale. Focus your awareness at the naval center. **Note:** *If this is too difficult, substitute the Downward Dog pose as described in step 8.*

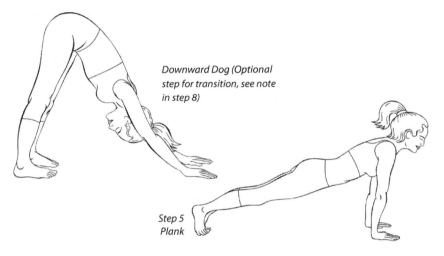

Downward Dog (Optional step for transition, see note in step 8)

Step 5 Plank

6. Exhale, let the knees come to the floor. Then bring the chest and chin to the floor keeping the buttocks elevated. Keep the palms of the hands next to the body to support the chin, chest, knees, and toes touching the floor. The back is slightly arched. For a moment in this pose the breath is held after the exhalation. Focus your awareness at the mid-section of the back and abdominal center.

Step 6 Eight-point Pose

7. Inhale, lower the hips while pressing the hands into the floor as you glide forward and lift the chest. The legs and the lower abdomen remain on the

Step 7
Cobra

floor. Firm the thighs and knee caps. The legs and feet should be well-extended. Arms can remain bent depending on flexibility. Focus your attention at the base of the spine and opening the chest.

8. Exhale, lower the chest. Gently slide back into a child's pose (optional). Or press through the hands, arms, and shoulders, lifting the buttocks so the body forms a triangle with the floor

Child's Pose (Optional step)

Step 8
Downward-
facing
Dog

making an inverted -V shape. Keep the neck flexible so that the eyes are looking toward the knees. Stay here for 3-5 breaths as you push down through the hands and the feet as the spine lengthens and remains neutral. The heels may or may not touch the floor. Focus your awareness at the throat area.

9. Inhale, step the left foot forward into a lunge again. Focus your awareness at the eyebrow area.

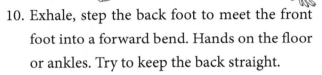

Step 10
Forward
Bend

Step 9
Lunge

10. Exhale, step the back foot to meet the front foot into a forward bend. Hands on the floor or ankles. Try to keep the back straight.

You may bend the knees. Focus your awareness at the pelvis. *Contra-indications: People with back conditions should not bend forward fully. Bend from the hips, keeping the spine straight. Use a chair or the wall as support.*

11. Inhale as you come up into an overhead stretch. When coming up, extend the arms out to the side, lifting up into an overhead stretch. Focus your awareness at the upper spine and throat area.

Step 11
Overhead
Stretch

12. Exhale and return to the standing posture (as in Step 1). Bring awareness to how you feel and regulate the breath before going on or ending the session.

Step 12
Standing
Pose

Summary

The sequence above is twelve poses with some that repeat. Here is a list of the poses. Do one or two if the entire sequence is too much for you.

- ❖ Prayer Pose (*Pranamasana*)

- ❖ Overhead Stretch (*Hastansana Urdhava* or Raised-arm Pose)

- ❖ Standing Forward Bend (*Uttanasana*)

- ❖ Lunge Pose (*Banarasana*)

❖ Plank Pose (*This is one of the most beneficial of all postures when it comes to developing core strength for your physical and psychological foundation. It requires core abdominal strength from the inside to the outside.*)

❖ Eight Point Pose (*Astavakrasana*)

❖ Cobra (*Bhujangasana*)

Note: *This practice can be used as a foundation practice to warm up for other practices you might want to do. It can be repeated several times but should be followed by a relaxation practice. It should be done on an empty stomach, either before food or 3-4 hours after eating. As with any practice, focus and direct your awareness and work within your capacity.*

"When the breath wanders,
the mind also is unsteady.
But when the breath is calm,
the mind too will be still,
and the yogi achieves long life.
Therefore, one should learn
to control the breath."
—SVATMARAMA,
HATHA YOGA PRADIPIKA

It's a Matter of Breath

Breath is the driving force behind our motivation and inspiration to live. In this lesson, we learn about breathing as the link between the body and mind, especially its power to calm, focus, and heal. Breathing correctly is of vital importance; nothing goes on without breath. It's our most basic and fundamental tool.

The breath is a vehicle that allows us to regulate our flow of vital energy as *pran, qi,* or life force. Termed *swara* in Sanskrit, these forces define the subtle energy beyond the physical air that flows in and out of our nostrils. When we're born, it's the breath that carries our life force in, and when we leave, it's the means by which we depart.

Keep in mind that pran and qi aren't the breath, but are the life force carried by the breath. This is why the breath is our most important companion. It provides the foundation for which we can learn to control and regulate our consciousness in totality and, ultimately, relax into being.

GET THE POWER IN HAND

You might wonder how the way you breathe affects your state of mind. It's quite simple. Think about when you were a child. When you went swimming, did you experience being underwater longer than expected? Did you panic? If so, it was an appropriate response.

Without breath, we die. It's the only active sense organ upon which our life depends.

Until recently, breathing wasn't popularly associated with health, although it was clear that life ended when a person stopped breathing. Thanks to the growing familiarity with yoga science, it now is more generally recognized that proper breathing is essential to physical as well as mental health.

The breathing process occurs automatically, like many other systems in the body. What distinguishes the respiratory network, which is in control of breathing, from other systems in the body is that we can have conscious control over it. While it differs from our renal or circulatory systems, the way we breathe can affect them.

Nothing goes on in our living organism without breath. Breathing is a process by which we take in oxygen through inhalation and release carbon dioxide through exhalation. Oxygen exchange takes place in the lungs, not solely via air but also through the lungs' blood flow.

Unlike the heart, the lungs aren't muscular. *(It might surprise you that the right lung has three lobes and the left has two.)* The motion of air into the lungs, as well as the movement of oxygen to our entire organ system, depends on a gradient in which air or oxygen moves from an area of higher concentration to one of lower concentration. The process of breathing works by this pressure gradient, as the outside air moves into the body by the chest cavity expanding and contracting.

For something as essential and "automatic" as our living breath, you might assume our bodies are programmed to use the optimal muscles to expand and contract the chest cavity. Think again. You have choices for which muscles to use. Most people make a habit of breathing with their chest and thoracic muscles, but this leaves them subject to erratic, unsteady, and anxiety-provoking breathing patterns.

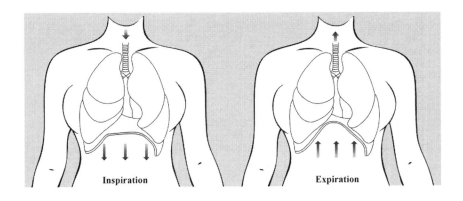

Inspiration   Expiration

The diaphragm muscle facilitates breathing. A large dome that actually expands to the size of the two lungs, this muscle separates the chest cavity from the abdominal cavity. When the diaphragm is contracted, it pushes air out of the lungs, and when expanded during inhalation, it draws air into the lungs. During inhalation, the diaphragm presses down on and massages the abdominal organs. Each exhalation, which is passive, allows these organs to resume their original position.

When the diaphragm is used for breathing, the chest remains motionless but other parts of the torso move slightly, particularly the abdomen if you're lying down or the rib cage when you're upright. As you refine your breathing, this motion becomes natural. Inhalation is active; exhalation is passive.

There are three ways breathing is influenced: metabolically, emotionally, and voluntarily. Metabolic breathing is an automatic and complex system involving the motor centers in our brain that is regulated by neurochemistry. The respiratory centers are located in the two lowest segments of our brain stem, the medulla and the pons. In addition, we have two other centers located in the heart known as peripheral chemoreceptors. Input from these centers is automatic; when we faint, the body will automatically start breathing again.

Emotions also influence our breathing. The limbic system in the brain is responsible for our emotional processing. It communicates with the cerebral cortex, which in turn wires us for our states of mind. For example, when we're fearful and become anxious, this center is sending signals to change respiration. This is why breath training is so necessary when we want to regulate how we feel.

Voluntary breathing—that which is directed consciously—is the only function of the autonomic nervous system that can be regulated through training. When we train our breath, respiration is directed by the mind. To see how this works, think of someone holding his breath, thanks to the cerebral cortex overriding metabolic functions.

It's widely known and accepted that breathing is the mechanical means for moving air in and out of the lungs so red blood cells can be replenished with oxygen. Yoga science, specifically swara yoga, has added another dimension to the breathing process. Simply put, it links our body and mind, and thus has a direct influence on whether we are calm and focused or distracted, disturbed, even mentally fatigued.

Relatively few people appreciate the way breathing affects their state of mind and energy.

We study this lesson early in our work because we must learn to deal with fluctuations in our mind as it copes with anxiety, depression, and distraction. Regulating and training our breath is a key to bringing us back to balance without side effects.

~~~

TRAVEL ON THE MIND-BODY BRIDGE

The operation of our nervous system makes breathing the bridge between our mind and body. To understand this concept, we examine breathing as it relates to the energy field we call *the mind*.

The autonomic nervous system maintains our energy balance or *homeostasis*. It has two branches: the *parasympathetic*, which controls the slowing of the heart rate, the regulation of digestion, and the clearing of toxins from the body, and the *sympathetic*, which controls our arousal mechanisms and prepares us to take action. The sympathetic system is involved when we're forced into action or feel sudden stress. For example, if we perceive ourselves in danger (stress), the sympathetic nervous system gears up for "fight or flight." Our body is prepared to do battle or escape. This action occurs through inhalation, not breath expiration. In the fight-or-flight response, our mind alerts the brain to the existence of danger. The body responds with an increased heart rate and adrenaline flowing into the bloodstream.

It's so interesting that both the parasympathetic and the sympathetic systems are automatically affected by the motion of our lungs. In a stressful situation, our breathing rate changes and we switch to chest breathing. Why? Because it brings in the air faster so we can move from danger. And when we breathe from the chest, we activate the sympathetic system. When we learn to breathe from the diaphragm, we keep the nervous system in a state of homeostasis, or balance. Thus the functioning of the autonomic nervous system is directly linked to the way we breathe.

When we breathe in, the brain receives a signal letting it know what sort of sympathetic response it will need. When we exhale, no signal is sent, and the parasympathetic branch of the nervous system will or will not have time to adjust to the situation.

Irregular and shallow breathing causes the same effect as the stress response. Again, it's important to be aware that the inhalation is the "habit" that sends the message. So when we're anxious, we take a quick breath and often hold it for a second or two. This signals the brain that we're in trouble. If we recognize this pattern, we bring our frontal cortex online and override the response, avoiding a full-blown anxiety attack. In this context, when we tell ourselves to "take a deep breath" before entering a stressful situation, we really should be saying, "Take a diaphragmatic breath."

If you consider some basic statistics about breathing, you'll have to agree that no day passes without our doing something of amazing consequence. We breathe in and out from 21,000 to 26,000 times per day at the rate of 16-18 times a minute. While it could be considered normal, this rate is not optimal for maintaining calm and balance. Breathing is a function so automatic that we rarely recognize the "good" and "bad" ways to do it. In fact, the way we breathe directly relates to our energy and mental state. If we use our diaphragm to breathe, the rate can be just 9,000 to 13,000 times per day. This healthy method of breathing supports a calm state of awareness and reduces wear and tear on the heart muscle.

TYPES OF BREATHING

Metabolic (Brain Stem) – Maintains normal blood gases; modifies respiration to meet energy demands from exercise, talking, eating

Emotional (Limbic Center) – Reflects pain, emotion, stress, temperature, our state of mind

Voluntary (Cerebral Cortex) – Singing, exercising, talking, eating, inhaling to smell something

Breath will continue without need to pay attention to it, but full awareness will allow you to manage this autonomic function. When you learn to bring breath under your conscious control, you can use it to regulate your vital functions—including your brain. Breath awareness can increase your mental stability.

Breathing is the only function in the autonomic nervous system that we can control consciously. I'll go more deeply into the psychological aspects of breath in later lessons, but here we simply want to become aware that there are different ways to breathe. Let's try the following simple experiment: Lie on your back and relax. Let the floor support your weight. Gently place the right or left hand over your navel. Begin breathing as you normally would. As you begin to inhale, the abdomen should expand like a balloon. *Don't make it inflate*; you're trying to see if it does so naturally. Exhale. Your abdomen should deflate. Did it? If so, you are already 75 percent of the way to feeling good, and you are reaping a number of beneficial effects.

PUT SOME WORK INTO RELAXING

Relaxation is an art that can be learned and a science that affects us on a physiological level. It involves both the body and mind and their interaction. In yoga class, it means lying down in *shavasana*, the corpse pose, and letting the weight of the body settle into the floor. However, this is only a small aspect of what relaxation really is.

Relaxation is, on one level, the letting go of tension in our skeletal muscles, which I will emphasize here. With practice, it can also transcend the physical aspect to where we can consciously control the letting go of many levels of tension, including our mind field, as we will see in other lessons.

Look at the word "relax." It's derived from the root "lax," which literally means "to loosen." When you're tense, a friend or colleague might suggest, "You should just loosen up." Physically you can loosen up by releasing the grip of your tense muscles, but on a mental and emotional level, you must loosen the grip on your thoughts. The purpose of relaxation is for the body—and especially the mind—to create space to rejuvenate.

From a physics perspective, we come back to homeostasis. Relaxation permits our system to return to equilibrium—a condition of vital stillness in which the mind is awake without being agitated. This in turn filters down to the brain, where stillness allows our neurochemicals to make needed repairs and to execute the thousands of other tasks they perform to support our communication pathways to and from the nervous system.

Relaxation may sound overly simple and easy to achieve, but those who try to relax often feel lost, not knowing where to start. Many equate relaxation with falling asleep or losing their awareness. Sleep doesn't allow for relaxation because our bodies and minds are constantly moving—tossing and turning during the night as well as engaging in activity through our dreams.

The practice of relaxation helps one learn how to rest. And the goal here is to rest, not sleep. We have all experienced waking from sleep feeling unrefreshed and strangely tired. That's because during sleep the body and mind were not in a state of relaxation and, thus, neither was rested. Knowing that relaxation is a learned skill requiring systematic training allows us to do something about the tension in our life, no matter how subtle or profound.

This lesson helps shed light on that aspect of relaxation. In order to relax enough to nourish and restore, we first must provide a restful posture for the body, then establish a proper breathing pattern, then systematically release the tension from individual body parts sequentially from head to toe. By systematically following a given sequence, the body and the mind ease into this state time and time again. A habit is established, and your life gains momentum.

I recall once listening to a "relaxation" CD on which the instructor repeated over and over, "Just breathe! Just breathe! Now relax!" These directives were not effective since they did not take into account the anatomy and physiology of relaxation. It's something we have to learn or relearn, as with diaphragmatic breathing, but being conscious of an inability to let go on your own and telling yourself to "relax, already!" doesn't generally accomplish much—except to make you even more uptight.

If all of this surprises you, you're not alone. When I began to apply the principles of relaxation in my daily life, I thought it was enough to let my body stop what it was doing. I didn't realize that relaxation is actually a different kind of activity, and that relaxation must be mental in order to manifest in the physical. Quieting our thoughts is necessary in order for the subtle energies to flow in a focused and calm manner, relaxing the physical body.

How does being aware or mindful affect our relaxation level? When tense, many unconsciously or consciously try to divert their attention from what's causing the issue. We do this by playing music, exercising, shopping, calling someone on the telephone or texting, etc. While these activities do take the mind from the situation causing the tension, a more sustainable approach is to train the mind and body to systematically "let go" or loosen the grip through our breath. Changing a mindset might appear counter-intuitive as a form of relaxation, but developing awareness is the way we can learn to root up what triggers tension and begin to nurture other habits. Breath awareness is the tool to accomplish this.

Stress caused by an environment of constant change makes relaxation essential to our health. We've seen that diaphragmatic breathing stabilizes our nervous system, and our nervous system is the key to regulating all functions of our body, which affects the mind's stability. When we relax, we become less tired, even when working 12-hour days. A relaxed breath creates a relaxed nervous system, which results in a clear, calm, and one-pointed mind. A relaxed person is able to direct his energy and move it in a way that helps him reach a goal.

For example, you decide to finish a lesson plan. When relaxed, you allow the energy to flow in the direction of completing the task. Relaxation creates space because the physical and the mental bodies have let go of tension, thereby allowing the flow of energy to take place.

Yoga (*asana*) is one such technique to accomplish this. People come into a movement class with a fixed amount of tension. If the class is taught skillfully, participants will release some of the tension reflected in their facial muscles. Singing or chanting removes tension by stimulating areas of the throat and the navel—two areas that become significantly tight when we hold tension. These positive effects last as long as a person's ability to hold the space for relaxation, which is why we create a systematic training to learn the skill. Over time, this skill can become a person's new reality and tension's grip will be loosened.

Relaxation is an ancient art and science, but many modern researchers have brought it to mainstream attention. Herbert Benson, MD, a cardiologist and founder of the Mind/Body Medical Institute at Massachusetts General Hospital in Boston, coined the term "the relaxation response" that validated the ancient teaching in yoga science for the Western scientific mind. His work in the 1970s clearly defines the steps to induce the physiological mechanisms that occur when a person brings his mind and body into a relaxed state by focusing on the breath and counting.

Yogis have done this for centuries. Benson's work applied the Western medical model by studying transcendental meditation practitioners and identifying their natural reflex responses after 20 minutes of daily meditation. Benson found that when study participants sat in a quiet environment and repeated a sound, they displayed less stress. He further reported that the relaxation response is beneficial for those suffering from hypertension, headaches, heart disease, anxiety, and other disorders, including drug addiction and PMS.[2]

The basic elements for eliciting the relaxation response from Benson's protocol aren't complex: a quiet environment, a comfortable position, a passive mental attitude, and repetition of a simple mental stimulus (a word, phrase, image, or prayer).

What about breath? This subject is so important that I need to re-emphasize it here. Most of us don't practice eliciting a relaxation response. We hope for relaxation, perhaps even yearn for it. And we may have discovered behaviors that foster it—a walk or bath, "unwinding" in front of the television, a glass of wine, or get-togethers with friends. But cultivating a practice—a regular, reliable way to remove tension and maintain balance—is different. As we've learned, it can be both brain- and body-sustaining.

THE NOSE KNOWS

My emphasis on the diaphragm doesn't mean the nose is insignificant. In fact, the airflow through our nasal passages stimulates our entire nervous system, including the brain. Inhalation not only stimulates olfactory nerves, it also triggers neuronal messages. Odors are connected to our emotions as a result of neurological connection in our nasal passages linked to the limbic system in the brain. Think of when you smelled something that reminded you of a happy time. Did it make you feel better? Being aware of this allows you to regulate your mood.

The nose is our major portal of breath into the body. It prepares and modifies breath for assimilation by the body and allows interaction with both the external and internal environment. The anatomical aspect of the nose via the mucosal membranes changes to meet the body's energy demands. The nose is so important that it warrants more attention than just being powdered or blown on occasion. Its health certainly should be cultivated.

The nose's mucus blanket picks up dust and debris and carries it out, making the nose a self-cleaning mechanism. But the many environmental elements we encounter can overwhelm the natural cleansing system of the nose. Nasal washes have been known to come to the rescue.

Use of a neti pot (*nasal cleanse in Sanskrit*) can help us cope with the effects of allergies, colds, and sinus problems. It detoxifies the nasal channel and, most important, affects the nervous system by directing air flow and bringing oxygen into the body and brain. The nasal wash changes the mucosal chemistry via the mucus production and soothes the mucosal tissue. For example, if the mucosa is irritated, the saline rinse will help calm the inflammation to change the inner anatomical surface and eventually air flow patterns.

Your nasal passage also must be kept lubricated so the mucus layer can block environmental toxins and a range of pests. It might not be obvious, but the quality of your nose's mucus is determined by diet. The types of foods you eat really can change the mucus composition in your nose. You have evidence of this process. Does your nose run when you eat something hot and spicy? Does ice-cold ice cream create a blocked feeling in your nasal passages?

Eat a good diet and use a saline solution that soothes and cleanses the nasal passages to bring vitality to your nose, as well as your brain and mind. See for yourself. Purchase a neti pot and practice washing your nasal passages for a week. My favorite is the original ceramic one from the Himalayan Institute.

As we have seen in this lesson, the basis for removing tension is modifying the breath and cleansing the nasal passages. With these skills, we can move on to understanding the importance of digestion in feeling good.

Review

TRUTH
Even, balanced breathing can remove obstacles in the mind.

OBSTACLE
Irregular breathing patterns create anxiety & disturbance.

EXIT STRATEGY
Make diaphragmatic breathing your default breath.

FACTS
- ❖ Breathing directs our emotional, physical & mental feelings.

- ❖ Breathing is the one autonomic nervous system activity we control.

- ❖ How we breathe affects our mind's balance.

- ❖ Diaphragmatic breathing is the basis for relaxation.

Path *of* Practice

"Inhale, and God approaches you.

Hold the inhalation, and God remains with you.

Exhale, and you approach God.

Hold the exhalation, and surrender to God."

—KRISHNAMACHARYA

 JOURNAL ACTIVITY

Purpose:

Become aware of your breathing pattern and record your progress for the breathing practices.

Technique:

Notice when your breath changes.

1. What happens when you become upset? What happens when you watch disturbing news on TV or listen to something sad? Can you maintain a steady breath in spite of the message you're receiving?

2. Record your progress daily after practicing each of the breathing practices. Your goal is to establish diaphragmatic breathing as your default breath and then use that to practice 1:1 and 2:1 breathing.

Note: *1:1—breathing with a ratio of one exhalation to one inhalation. For example, exhale for a count of 2 and inhale for a count of 2. Choose the count based on your comfort level.*

2:1—breathing with a ratio of two exhalations to one inhalation. For example, exhale for a count of 4 and inhale for a count of 2.

Do these practices for 3-5 minutes at a pace that allows you to remain calm and balanced. If you feel out of breath you have exceeded your capacity.

Core Practices

DIAPHRAGMATIC BREATHING

The focus is diaphragmatic breathing, which is both energizing and relaxing. The breathing apparatus includes the trachea, which allows air to pass into the lungs; the lungs, which are the organs where gas exchange takes place; the diaphragm, which lengthens and shortens the chest cavity; and the rib cage, which creates the structure and protection of the breathing apparatus. When learning diaphragmatic breathing, it's best to learn in stages so you can develop a new habit of breathing. Focus and breath are the two key principles that support a relaxed mind. This is the simplest and most profound way to learn systematic relaxation. By focusing one's attention on the breath, you get the physiological benefits as well as the systematic training of the mind.

Purpose:

To establish diaphragmatic breathing.

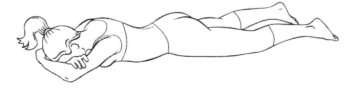

Technique:

1. We begin in the Crocodile Pose (*Markarasana*). In this pose, you rest on the abdomen with a rolled-up blanket across the upper chest and under the armpits. This supports the upper

body so you can relax the neck, shoulders, and upper back into the position. The head rests on the folded arms above the head and in front. The legs are about 6-10 inches apart, with the feet turned out or in, based on the preference for comfort.

2. Rest here and begin inhaling and exhaling. As you inhale, you'll feel the abdomen pressing into the floor and the back expanding and rising. As you exhale, the abdomen will contract and relax, and the back will sink and relax. You may also notice that the rib cage will expand on the inhale and contract and relax on the exhale.

3. Now roll over onto the back. In this pose, the Corpse Pose (*Shavasana*), rest on the back with a thin cushion under the head to keep the neck neutral with the head in alignment with the spine. *If you have back discomfort, you can roll a blanket or put a bolster under the knees to take the stress off the psoas muscle and relax the back.* The arms are placed slightly away from the body and the fingers are facing upward. Legs are in a relaxed, comfortable position 6-10 inches apart—again, based on comfort.

4. Rest here, inhaling and exhaling. As you inhale, you'll feel the abdomen expand as if you're filling a balloon. As you exhale, it will relax and deflate. You may feel the ribs (ever so slightly toward the back) expand on an inhale and contract on an exhale.

5. If you have difficulty feeling the abdomen move, you may take the hands over the head. This immobilizes the chest so you're unable to use its muscles while inhaling and exhaling.

6. Do this for 5-10 minutes daily until you feel comfortable and relaxed in this breathing position. (As you become more advanced and want to strengthen the diaphragm muscle, you can use a sand bag. I recommend you work with a teacher to show you its exact positioning.)

NASAL-WASH

Purpose:

To clean the nasal passages with salt water to facilitate unobstructed breathing required for all practices. It also helps to keep the mucus membranes moist and healthy to eliminate colds.

Technique:

Saline Solution: Mix a heaping 1/4 tsp. of finely ground non-iodized grey sea salt or a slightly rounded 1/2 tsp. of coarsely ground salt (kosher salt) in the neti pot with 8 ounces of warm sterilized water until the salt is completely dissolved.

Position:

Turn the head to one side over the sink, keeping the forehead at the same height as the chin, or slightly higher.

1. Gently insert the spout in the upper nostril so it forms a seal. Raise the neti pot so the saline solution flows out the lower nostril. If it drains from the mouth, lower the forehead in relation to the chin.

2. When the neti pot is empty, face the sink and exhale vigorously without pinching the nostrils.

3. Refill the neti pot and repeat on the other side. Again, exhale vigorously to clear the nasal passages.

4. Do one or more of the recommended exercises to drain any remaining saline solution.

    a. Forward Bending
    b. Alternate Toe Touching

Note: *If you have nasal blockages, consult a health care practitioner before trying this practice. It's best to have a demonstration before trying this on your own.*

"Yoga is an effortless dance
with breath and gravity."
—VANDA SCARAVELLI

"Laughter aids the digestion. You can eat a huge stew with your schoolmates and digest it with no bother at all, whereas you can get indigestion eating a leaf of lettuce in boring company."
—MAURICE MESSÉGUÉ
OF PEOPLE AND PLANTS: THE AUTOBIOGRAPHY OF EUROPE'S MOST CELEBRATED HEALER

It's a Matter of Digestion

N ow that we understand the mechanism of our habits, the importance of breath and who we are, we're prepared to begin the work to gain access to our energy source.

The gut has the most profound impact on our health and well-being. It's the basis for our nourishment, which translates into our energy, focus, and ability to carry out our life's purpose. Our diet has a tremendous effect on the quality of our digestion and, as a result, on the quality of our consciousness. The elements of healthy digestion will also be examined in this lesson.

DEVELOP A HEALTHY APPETITE

Digestion takes place through both a mechanical process, called *peristalsis*, and chemical processes—the enzymatic reactions that metabolize nutrients. To optimize digestion, we can work anatomically through movement of the abdominal cavity, as well as utilize herbs and other nutrients. This will enhance and support the chemical reactions that take place in the breakdown of food.

The average person may be quite unaware whether the food he eats is actually being well-digested, mentally or physically. Even when he knows the process, he might feel powerless to change some digestive aspects to promote healthy and vibrant thinking, feeling, and being. It just isn't common knowledge.

Have you ever thought about what food your body and mind really want? Or really need? *Want* doesn't always correlate with *need*. Do you know what your body and mind require to carry out the functions you plan? Ayurveda and even allopathic medicine, to some extent, acknowledge that people who eat less live longer. We need to take in just the right amount—not too much, not too little.

Let's consider what we need as a minimum to feel good physically and mentally. How much protein, fats and carbohydrates, vitamins, and minerals do we require? What herbs and homeopathic remedies, how much physical activity and meditation should we include for our mental well-being? To feel good, we must determine all these things and how they correlate with what we feed our mind. We not only require nourishment, but must also properly digest it.

We don't have to be scientists to see how the health of our gastrointestinal tract and the process of digestion affect our thinking and feeling—and the other way 'round. For example, an upset stomach creates a nervous brain. An irritated stomach or intestine creates anger and irritation, and an overly gassy gut creates a foggy mind. I don't think anyone would disagree that all of our moods are either created by faulty digestion of the gut or faulty digestion in the mind.

~~~

EATING IS A BALANCING ACT

When we eat, *what* we eat, and *how* we eat should be carefully addressed when looking at tuning our digestive function to work efficiently to support our entire mind-brain matrix. These three diet components determine the power of our physical and mental digestion. The concepts revolve around the rules of nature because, as we know, nature is in constant search of homeostasis, or balance.

When we eat in tune with our metabolic clock, we focus on eating the bulk of our food during midday, when the sun is at its highest. Eating foods grown without chemicals, artificial genetic modification, and synthetic processing supports the colonies of bacteria that inhabit our—gastrointestinal tract—to protect us from environmental invaders. Eating with full awareness allows us to choose how much to eat and keeps our body and mind in harmony and balance. We can determine when it's best to eat if we understand that timing is everything.

We look to the Chinese system of medicine that finds energy flows through meridians or channels in a specific pattern. For this lesson, I'll address energy flow as it relates to digestive capacity.

Every two hours, a different organ dominates the body. According to the Traditional Chinese Medicine (TCM) model, the small intestine energy flow is dominant from 1-3 p.m. Since it is the organ primarily for digestion and absorption of nutrients, the window from 1-3 p.m. is the best time for the food that we ate earlier to be assimilated. The large intestine energy flow dominates from 5-7 a.m., discarding the body's toxic waste. That makes early morning the most appropriate time to eliminate.

TCM CHART

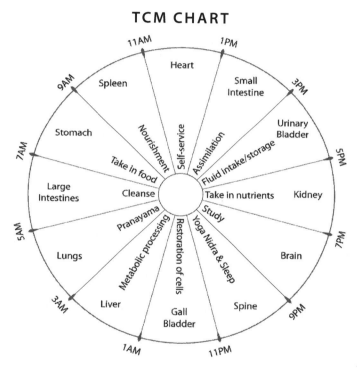

In the Ayurvedic system of medicine, a 24-hour cycle is divided into six segments, not 12, but the principle is essentially the same: If we follow the energy patterns during the day with respect to our bodily functions, our mind will maintain balance and allow energy to flow freely.

For example, in the mornings between 6 and 10 o'clock, we

feel most energetic or fresh. What we eat during this time should be cleansing and light to avoid impeding our mental energy. Test yourself. Many people feel they need food as soon as they get up, but convince yourself to eat just a piece of fruit or drink fresh homemade juice accompanied by a handful of cooked toasted oats.

AYURVEDIC CHART

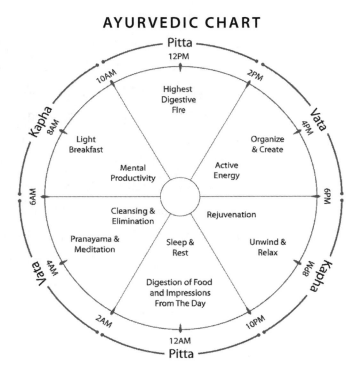

Take note of how good food tastes in the next phase of the cycle. From 10 a.m. to 2 p.m., our metabolic energy is at its highest. Digestive enzymes are up-regulated (activated) so food burns most efficiently. During this time, eat anything you want, but be careful not to eat too much since you don't want to smother the fire of digestion. I always suggest to students that if they need to have sweets or a dessert, this is the time to do it.

During the last cycle, from 2-6 p.m., we feel active and light, in some cases even light-headed. Here we have a tendency to go for sugar and other stimulating foods, since it's the end of the day and we need a boost. It's far better to choose stabilizing and moist food, which generally means complex foods. For example, whole grains regulate blood sugar levels and "moist" foods don't require water to be washed down. Choose fresh fruit over dry fruit; cooked vegetables over raw; baked potatoes over potato chips; oatmeal over sugary cereal; whole-grain bread over white bread. Eat soups and protein-rich foods, but avoid stimulating foods that contain caffeine or sugar, as in coffee and dessert.

Take a quick look at the overnight fast. The energy cycle repeats itself through the next 12 hours, but instead of repeating the food intake of the day, don't eat anything at all. (Plain water or water with lemon or some herbal tea is the exception.) The reason for doing this is that the digestive system needs rest for at least 12 hours daily, and an overnight "fast" is the way to ensure this is accomplished. How easy is it to get up in the morning after a late-night meal?

From a physiological viewpoint, the period from dinner to breakfast is the optimal time for the body to do its major housecleaning. When you eat a late-night meal, you end up feeling sluggish in the morning because the housecleaning was not done. If you think of the intervals between daytime meals as times for dusting, then night-time is for sweeping. Not eating before going to sleep allows the metabolic processes to work most efficiently.

If, for whatever reason, you must have something before bed-time, try taking just a glass of water or water with lemon, then herbal teas (without caffeine), and lastly, milk that has been boiled for three minutes to aid digestion. The night-time "fast" enables us to digest excess material from the day, restore cellular function, and repair any damage to the digestive system. Our fat stores begin to break down, too, which is why you would gain more weight eating at night than eating the same amount during the day.

From what we've learned, it's clear that the best time for our brain and our mind field to recharge is between meals, preferably at night. Our energy and flexibility are highest in the morning and early evening, when our stomachs are not overloaded and our vitality flows. Americans, though, are a nation of grazers. Marketing tells us to eat many meals a day to keep the engines running. This is true, but keeping the engines running without rest wears them out faster and our vitality wanes. We pay little or no attention to our metabolic clock. And since we eat throughout the day, we give little thought to the best time for food or rest.

This is a *"crime against wisdom."* Try to eat as I recommend, and I assure you that your mood and brain health will improve. Eat at the right time, rest, and exercise your body. Your physical and mental vitality and overall sense of well-being will increase.

TAKE A FRESH APPROACH TO FOOD

Having established the habit of healthy meal times, we move on to paying attention to the quality of food we eat. A nourished brain feeds a vital mind and vice versa. The food we eat ultimately is incorporated into our consciousness—our mind. How we feel depends on the physical energy derived from our food, but the subtle quality of that food determines our state of mind—either calm and focused or disturbed and distracted.

Since 1916, the U.S. Department of Agriculture had recommended the food groups necessary for an adequate diet. In 1992, the food groups officially were organized into a "food guide pyramid." Bread, cereal, rice, and pasta were at the bottom; fruits, vegetables, meats, and dairy products were in the middle; and fats, oils, and sweets were at the top. The pyramid was intended as an outline for what to eat each day and in what amounts. Generally, we were to eat more of those at the bottom and less of those at the top.

In 2011, the USDA issued long-overdue new dietary guidelines that replaced the food pyramid with the My Plate Model comprised of about 30 percent grains, 30 percent vegetables, 20 percent fruits, and 20 percent proteins, accompanied by a small circle to the upper left representing dairy. However, agricultural-governmental interests could slightly distort the model, so we should go beyond what the government advises. We should consider what a feel-good food-plate model would look like for our unique bio-psychological matrix.

The brain/mind-nourishing diet is somewhat different, in that it substitutes beans for most animal-derived protein; limits dairy consumption to no other than organic and not necessarily low fat; emphasizes fresh food and whole grains; and eliminates or minimizes white-flour products and genetically modified products, with gluten-modified wheat being at the top of the list.

The components of food may be classified as macronutrients (carbohydrates, proteins, fats), and micronutrients (vitamins, minerals, phytochemicals), with micronutrients playing a vital role in the metabolism of the macronutrients. But food is more than just its physical components. It has essence, as well, just as we do. Fresh food has the life force still present within it, so its nutrients can be easily assimilated, adding to our own life force—our energy.

When the food we eat has been concentrated through the process of dehydration, genetically modified or preserved with chemicals to prolong its shelf life, it contains the physical constituents but not its life force. We will still be eating carbohydrates, proteins, and fats.

When you consume vitamin supplements, according to the allopathic reductionist theory, you're "satisfying" your brain's basic needs. We might be getting the correct molecules, but as a Traditional Chinese or Ayurvedic model of medicine has pointed out—and many Western-trained biochemists agree—these supplements won't be giving you the energy or that vital force you need. We'll feel heavy and dull—essentially devitalized.

If we persist in eating this way over an extended time, we'll feel older than our years, because our system will lack the components to restore the vital energy that supports our mind-brain complex. For that reason, I warn on the use of canned foods. I oppose microwaving, too. I believe microwave preparation changes the molecular form of foods because, simply put, the food's taste changes.

As we will see in a later lesson, taste has a profound physical and psychological effect. No one knows the effect of that not-so-subtle change to the assimilation process on the biological level. My guess is that microwaving would alter the way food is incorporated into cells.

I advise my students and clients who feel mental fatigue and fogginess to stick with preparing fresh foods daily using natural heat. If they don't have access to fresh food preparation, I suggest frozen foods that need to be cooked.

The value of fresh foods will be obvious after a simple experiment. For three days, if you can tolerate it, eat only pre-prepared foods. For the next three days, eat only fresh food. Take note of your energy, the speed of your responses, and your overall emotional state. I promise you'll recognize a huge difference that will make processed foods seem distasteful to you.

Is this exercise too arduous? Here's a low-risk, quicker contest. Sample some freshly squeezed juice and then taste the same kind of juice from a can, container, or bottle. How do you feel? This may be an eye-opening experience.

If fresh food is the equivalent of 200 volts of energy, processed food and genetically modified food gives off 25 volts or next to zero. But simply eating fresh foods isn't enough; they must be prepared correctly with the right ingredients. Why are preparation and the right ingredients so important? Keep in mind that our soil is systematically being demineralized; pollutants fill our air and water; and now even the seeds of our grains are being injected with pesticides and animal DNA. So when we eat fresh food, we still may not be getting the required basic nutrients; or trace minerals like iodine, selenium, and zinc; or even the quality necessary for our consciousness to reach a calm and focused state.

I want to stress the importance of good nutrition in regulating our mood and brain. "Devitalized" food and inadequate amounts of trace minerals and vitamins leave the average person's brain energy-impaired and produce an imbalanced mind.

When we're young, our natural resiliency can't be completely subdued by an improper diet, but this is no longer true as we age. Cellular mechanisms change, and it becomes obvious how all our functions are linked to our dietary practices. Correcting our diet, even after years of processed foods and canned juices, can do wonders for our overall brain health and our cognitive and emotional capacity. If this book does nothing other than convince you to eat better to feel good, it will have achieved much of its purpose.

HOW MUCH IS ENOUGH?

I speak about quantity as the last element because it seems to be the most difficult to ascertain. How many times have you said to yourself, "Stop eating, you don't need anymore"? How long did it take for you to realize that eating a full meal before a mental task inhibits your ability to focus and concentrate? Obvious questions with obvious answers pointing to one conclusion: Too much food—even if it's the *right* food—and a clear, sharp mind are antithetical.

When we eat too much, we directly interfere with our energy

flow, and that makes our mind dull and stupefied. Excess causes loss of vitality, dulls our awareness, blunts our alertness, and produces fatigue. In fact, it was Hippocrates who said, "Everything in excess is opposed by nature." Do you think it's possible to feel good after consuming a four-course meal? Eating that much makes it difficult just to get up from the table!

Sometimes we overeat, in spite of suspecting that we would enjoy the food more if we could moderate. We understand that excess food doesn't translate into additional nutrients, yet we eat to excess. The fifth bit of chocolate cake tastes no different from the first because our taste receptors are bound and no longer respond, yet we shovel the cake into our mouth. Actually, we tend to overeat foods that aren't nourishing for our brain or mind. Our digestive systems generally find non-nourishing foods nutritionally unsatisfying and so, paradoxically, we crave more.

By overeating, we put a strain not only on our digestive system, which can't accommodate the plethora of food, but also on our brain, nervous system, and our consciousness. Trying to operate on any level—physically, creatively, emotionally, intellectually—is far more difficult if the body is trying to figure out what to do with the food it has just taken in.

And yet, I don't recommend undereating either, because it can cause a decline in optimal functional mental capacity. By "undereating" I mean not getting enough nutrients for proper brain function. This isn't the same as cutting down on calories, because caloric restriction can increase life span. (Conversely, too much restriction can decrease it.) I'm talking about skipping meals and drinking diet soda and coffee to curb appetite, basically to take the place of missed meals. When we starve our brains on a regular basis in an attempt to stay thin, we're actually causing physical and mental stress to our system. Indeed, overdieting by skipping meals is one of the most hazardous threats to our mental state and overall vitality.

What we should strive for is balance—when our organism is in homeostasis—so we become consciously aware (calm) of the process and feel vital and alive. We'll be at full capacity for playing, thinking, and feeling good—simply for living. When we understand the mechanics of digestion, we can follow the forces of our metabolic clock.

Review

TRUTH
Optimal digestion is a step to feeling good.

OBSTACLE
Mental & physical distress from improper eating.

STRATEGY
Eating by our metabolic clock to restore healthy functions.

FACTS

❖ *When* we eat affects the quality of digestion.

❖ *What* we eat affects our quality of consciousness.

❖ *How much* we eat affects our energy.

❖ Eating with digestion in mind helps food to serve as medicine.

Path *of* Practice

"For a genuine and everlasting transformation, one must practice a systematic method of self-discipline and self-training. Mere philosophy and intellectual knowledge cannot stand in time of need, if one does not know how to use the essentials of that philosophy in one's daily life. Applying theoretical knowledge and living with it in daily life is called practice."

—SWAMI RAMA

 JOURNAL ACTIVITY

Purpose:

To evaluate and record moods and energy-level changes after practicing the overnight fast.

Technique:

1. Record your results from practicing the overnight fast (*see below*).

2. Pay attention to how you feel, especially in the morning; how you sleep; your craving; and your appetite in general.

THE OVERNIGHT FAST

Purpose:

To rest the physical digestive system and train the mind to be still.

Technique:

1. Stop eating after 6:30 p.m. This requires a few guidelines for success. Assess your situation. Do you eat close to bedtime? Do you wake up fatigued? Do you carry excess weight? Do you have trouble sleeping? To practice the overnight fast, you must be in a healthy state.

2. Have one or two freshly prepared meals per day, with a complete lunch that includes a protein source, veg-

etable source, and something raw, like a salad or fruit. The body needs nutrients to clean and detox. You can't practice the overnight fast if you only ate a salad for lunch. There won't be enough nutrients to sustain you.

3. Include freshly made teas like ginger, tulsi, peppermint, and pure water throughout the day. Teas have many compounds that help to ignite cleansing and nourishing mechanisms. Water helps with hydration, and we know that our water channels move wastes through our system. So including water and freshly made herbal teas could help to flush any toxins from the air that we breathe, as well as the chemical residues from the food that we ingest. These can act as a stimulant to encourage snacking and eating throughout the day into the evening.

4. Use supplements skillfully, based on your need. If you're under stress, you'll be expending your B vitamins, so you may want to include them in your supplementation. If you're looking for sugar, you might not be taking in enough protein through your diet. If you crave fats, you may need to add some omega-3s in your diet. These are just some examples. We usually search for food when we have an underlying deficiency.

5. Learn to enjoy family and friends, and meditate. Fill your eating time with family, relaxation, and meditation. Your liver will love it.

Core Practice

The practice in this lesson begins to bring our awareness to the abdominal region (hara), the place where we physically digest our food but also generate our core vitality and stamina. Working with this area begins to reinforce and strengthen our core foundation. We then obtain the awareness to access the subtle forces that help us maintain our emotional and psychological well-being. Keep in mind that all practices throughout the lessons are best done on an empty stomach, either before eating or 3-4 hours afterward.

WORKING WITH THE PELVIC TILT (PHASE 1)

Purpose:

To gain awareness of the entire pelvic area from the base to the navel center. The pelvic/abdominal area holds all the digestive organs, as well as the associated emotions.

Technique:

1. Lie on your back with the feet flat on the floor, about hip distance apart. Closer is better than being too far apart. Have the arms resting by the side with the palms down. You may have to use a small pillow under the head.

2. Press the soles of the feet into the floor and be aware of the inner thigh muscles. Relax the head, neck, and belly as you maintain an even and slow breath.

3. Follow the exhalation and inhalation with a slight pelvic rocking motion. As you exhale, squeeze the abdominal muscles and navel toward the spine; as you inhale, let it relax and release.

4. Be aware (as you exhale and squeeze the abdominal muscles) that the back flattens on the floor. Be aware, when you release as you inhale, that the back releases off the floor and the abdominal muscles relax. There is a gentle rocking motion. Once you establish this even flow of breath with the movement of the abdomen, you can keep the pelvis stable and just squeeze and release.

5. Next, add the dimension of the pelvic floor. As you exhale, contract the lower belly, drawing the muscles of the pelvic floor together, and then lift up toward the navel and press back toward the spine.

6. Become aware of the energy lifting from the inner thighs through the pelvic floor and to the lower, middle, and upper abdomen. Repeat this sequence a few times.

7. Now turn over on the abdomen and assume the Crocodile Position with diaphragmatic breathing as you relax the entire body. On an exhalation, roll the buttocks toward each other as deeply and intensely as you can. Inhale and release. Be aware

to isolate only the buttocks when you contract. Repeat several times.

8. Next, repeat the process, but this time, on exhalation engage the entire pelvic floor, including the anal sphincter and urinary sphincter as you pull up and in toward the spinal column. Inhale and relax. Repeat several times.

9. Next, sit back on the heels with the tops of the feet flat on the floor. Bend forward to rest the abdomen and chest on the thighs. You can use a pillow between the abdomen and chest for more flexibility.

10. Rest the forearms on the floor in front of you. If the spine allows, the forehead can also rest on the floor.

11. If the knees are uncomfortable, place a folded blanket between the calves and thighs. A blanket or cushion can also be placed under the ankles to ease discomfort. Rest here for a few moments before standing up.

"Yoga teaches us to cure what need
not be endured and endure
what cannot be cured."
—B.K.S. IYENGAR

"The longer I live, the less confidence I have in drugs and the greater is my confidence in the regulation and administration of diet and regimen."

—JOHN REDMAN COXE

It's a Matter of Chemistry

We look at the physical and chemical aspects of digestion in this lesson. There is an elaborate process for digesting our food that ultimately becomes our medicine. The way we take in food elements from the outside requires that our digestive system has the intelligence to transform the gross food matter into usable elements to nourish our entire organism.

This lesson incorporates both the concrete or physical and the less tangible or subtle aspects of our digestion—our inner tube for healing. We'll be able to understand and respect what this independent system does for us on an hourly basis after eating.

THIS IS A LOT TO DIGEST

Here we learn how food is used during digestion and, going through each step, we'll see how the process is key to optimal physical and psychological immunity (resilience). Depending on the three components—timing of eating, quality, and quantity of food—digestion will take about six hours over six stages. That doesn't mean we should eat every six hours because the digestive system should rest when not taking in food.

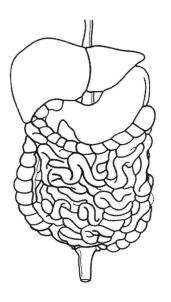

Our digestive system is a 21-foot inner tube that connects us to the outside world. Through both physical and chemical processes it brings nourishment and protection to our entire organism. Digestive function begins immediately when we put something in the mouth and begin to chew. The mouth, pharynx, and esophagus are responsible for ingesting, chewing, and swallowing. We experience taste via the mouth and nose when food is mixed with saliva. According to Ayurvedic medicine, taste alone has a direct impact on the physical and subtle functions that occur in the body and mind. With this in mind, we acknowledge the taste changes that occur at each stage of the digestive process.

In this earliest stage of eating, the **sweet** taste predominates. The physical act of chewing prepares the organism (our body) by sending signals to the brain via the tongue and jaw muscles in advance of the food's downward journey for further processing. This stage in the chewing mechanism is crucial for the chemical and mechanical processes. During chewing, the food becomes surrounded with saliva, which contains a protective substance called *immunoglobulin.* This antibody provides defense from foreign invaders that could inhabit the healthy bacterial colonies dwelling below.

If our food is a carbohydrate, the saliva begins to break down the sugar into smaller molecules via an enzyme called *ptyalin.* I believe this happens first because the brain's major fuel is a simple sugar, glucose, and if the sugar initially is reduced to a smaller unit, it will keep the brain fed while the rest of the process is occurring.

"The digestive canal is in its task a
complete chemical factory."
—Ivan Petrovich Pavlov

Although digestion is really only thought of as a physical process, keep in mind that our emotions can affect digestion at all stages, beginning with this first stage. Too much worry, anxiety, fear, and stress can result in a decrease in saliva compounded with a dry tongue, which also interferes with digestion. So saliva, if healthy and balanced, will protect our organism. The tongue is obviously very useful at this time since it allows us to taste food, which engages the receptors in the brain, which in turn signal the organ systems throughout our body based on the taste that was experienced.

SIX STAGES, SIX TASTES

Taste has a profound impact on the mind. As the digestion process progresses, each of the six tastes identified by the Ayurvedic medical model—sweet, sour, salty, pungent, bitter, astringent—presents itself at some point. This is why it's so important to permit our food to digest completely before bringing in more so the process is not disrupted.

Pay attention to the message in what we've just considered, because it debunks the theory that we should eat several small meals throughout the day. It's not what nature intended and actually weakens digestion.

The next phase involves food traveling to the stomach via the esophagus, where both solid and liquid further break it down in a ripening effect, if you will. The stomach is a thick-walled sac—a storage unit—no bigger than the palm of our hand when empty. The stomach is designed to mechanically churn and massage the food, sterilize it, and perform chemical digestion before letting the food proceed.

The digestive system uses both mechanical and chemical processes to provide nourishment to our organism. This is important to know because then we can approach working with our gastrointestinal system (GI system) with nutrients as well as physical movements. This is one of the reasons why I focus the movement portion of workshop lessons on the abdominal area—"hara."

Concerning the chemical reactions, our stomach secretes enzymes, namely *pepsinogen* (inactive form), which is activated to *pepsin* in the stomach. The substance is responsible for breaking down proteins into smaller peptides. An enzyme, called *rennin* in infants and *gastric lipase* in adults, is responsible for the digestion of milk proteins here, too. The gastric juices at this stage destroy any additional unwanted bacteria that may have escaped the mouth.

Now the sweet stage of digestion that occurred in the mouth is changed to **sour** due to the presence of hydrochloric acid. This also begins to minimize the feeling of fullness we experience during the early stage of the process. It's noteworthy that little gastric juice is produced in response to habits like consuming tasteless, low quality food or eating too fast, and that affects digestion. Symptoms of faulty processes at this point include nausea, vomiting, belching, bloating, pain, or stomach ache. This distressed digestive state often reflects our emotional condition and can affect it.

From a Traditional Chinese Medicine perspective, the stomach is the organ responsible for ripening and receiving the food and fluids. It's active from 7-9 a.m., when it's ready to collect food. When we worry, generate excessive thinking, feel stressed, eat late at night, or eat too quickly, the stomach energy meridian becomes depleted and stagnant, resulting in nausea and irritation or even burning pain, as mentioned above.

"The stomach is an integral part of the digestive system, but it's not the same in all animals. Some animals have stomachs with multiple compartments. (They're often mistakenly said to have multiple stomachs.) Cows and other "ruminants"—including giraffes, deer and cattle—have four-chambered stomachs, which help them digest their plant-based food. But some animals—including seahorses, lungfishes and platypuses—have no stomach. Their food goes from the esophagus straight to the intestines."
—JOSEPH CASTRO, *LIFE SCIENCE*, OCT. 4, 2013

NO STOMACH FOR THIS

When food leaves the stomach, it becomes *chyme* and proceeds to the small intestine. This highly specialized organ has a huge surface area of circular folds lined with hundreds of thousands of hair-like projections (microvilli) that contain tiny blood vessels, called the *intestinal brush border*. This brush border is said to support approximately 1,700 microvilli on each epithelial cell. The design is meant to increase the surface area of the small intestine so maximum absorption can take place. Some say it increases the absorptive capacity of the cells 30- to 40-fold. Quite astonishing, and it explains why we need to keep this area of our GI track cleansed and nourished. The surface area is far from small—between 6 and 7 meters—but its designation relates to its diameter compared to the large intestine.

The small intestine has three divisions, each with its own specialization. The top portion, or *duodenum,* is where the primary breakdown of food particles occurs as they pass from the stomach and iron is absorbed. Here the chyme from the stomach mixes with secretions from the liver and pancreas to digest fats and proteins. The upper small intestine helps break down larger food stuffs into useable molecules with the help of the liver and pancreas.

Bile salts from the liver assist in the emulsification of fats, while pancreatic enzymes digest proteins into smaller units called *peptides.* It's here that the **salty** taste is predominant as the result of a mixture of acid and alkaline. After food is processed in the upper small intestine (*duodenum*), it proceeds to the lower part of the small intestine, the *jejunum.* In this place, the activity of fire heightens, and it's where the greatest nutrient absorption takes place thanks to longer villi. More concentrated enzymes and transport carrier proteins exist here. Digested food becomes more yellow and brown in color as it becomes more **pungent**.

At this stage, there's increased intestinal circulation resulting from the body producing more heat by what is termed *the inner fire of metabolic combustion.* In yoga science, the subtle movement of energy that occurs at this phase is called *samana vayu*—the sideways-moving energy between the navel and the diaphragm. Too many meals eaten at the wrong times can throw off the movement. The habit of many Americans to eat and forage with small meals throughout the day looks more detrimental in light of this information.

The final phase of the small intestine is the fifth stage of the digestive process and occurs when the bulk of the matter proceeds to the *ileum*, the longest portion of the small intestine. Further digestion occurs via bile, which carries the **bitter** taste. Here's where vitamin B12 and bile salts are absorbed through the villi of the ileum wall.

The movement of energy that occurs at this phase is called the *apana vayu,* the downward movement of energy from the naval to the perineum, to aid in elimination. The process helps things move downward and out of the body. It's a major subtle energy current that is needed for cleansing and detoxing, cleansing both mind and body.

This is when we might feel empty or light and want to eat again. Resist the feeling, as doing so would put unnecessary stress on the system.

How do we know if the small intestine isn't functioning properly? As when the stomach fails to function correctly, we may experience more than normal abdominal rumbling or lack of it; constipation or diarrhea; and ulcers could erupt on the tongue.

As with all digestive organs, the Traditional Chinese Medicine model views the small intestine as an organ that transforms food with the assistance of the spleen and kidney meridian. It can be indirectly affected by emotions, such as anger, irritability, and animosity, as they cause the liver to stagnate. Anxiety and stress can also interrupt the proper flow of the liver's many processes. In that condition, the liver can become stuck or be sluggish in performing its many duties, such as storing glycogen, the storage form of glucose (remember that glucose is the master fuel for the brain);

helping break down fats via lipase; producing bile; and many other metabolic tasks.

The last and sixth stage of digestion is when the bulk of the matter proceeds to the large intestine, where it is designed to extract and absorb water, as well as reabsorb vitamins and minerals. It is here where most of the vitamins that weren't already absorbed are reprocessed by bacteria and released in a form that can be absorbed by the body, as with vitamin K. The waste products are eliminated, and the **astringent** taste becomes prominent. As in the small intestine, there are communities of 100 trillion microbial colonies (microflora) that protect and nourish our entire GI mucosa and epithelia. Peristalsis further encourages the downward movement of fecal matter, which is bacteria, both dead and alive.

How do we know if the large intestine is not functioning properly? Constipation, excessive gas, and diarrhea are clues. If we experience emotions of worry and sadness, we can be assured that our large intestine will be compromised.

Some microbes promote health while others cause disease. Microbes play an essential role in metabolizing nutrients, vitamins, drugs, hormones—and cancer-causing agents. The integrity of the microflora in the intestinal tract determines the health of our brain and our overall health. For that reason, when we overeat or drink too much, we add to the burden of the microflora and, like a car with inferior oil, our brain can't run at peak efficiency.

In our next lesson, we complete our digestive journey, bringing us to the basis of how food is indeed medicine through the functioning of our microflora—the gut microbiome.

Review

TRUTH
The physical digestion process is a health barometer.

OBSTACLE
Faulty habits create faulty function.

STRATEGY
Eat to support the phases of digestion.

FACTS

❖ Our gastrointestinal tract is 21-25 feet from mouth to anus.

❖ It has 100 million more neurons than our spinal column.

❖ It has every neurotransmitter class found in the brain.

❖ It has the greatest amount of immune tissue.

Path *of* Practice

"It has long been known for sure that the sight of tasty food makes a hungry man's mouth water; also, lack of appetite has always been regarded as an undesirable phenomenon, from which one might conclude that appetite is essentially linked with the process of digestion."

—IVAN PAVLOV

 JOURNAL ACTIVITY

Purpose:

To assess and record moods and energy level changes after including Kitchari in diet.

Technique:

1. Record your results from eating Kitchari diet for a series of three days. (*recipe, see below*).

2. Pay attention to how you feel, especially in the morning, how you sleep, your cravings and your appetite in general.

THE KITCHARI DIET

 Purpose:

To rest and rekindle the digestive system.

• RECIPE •

Kitchari is a mixture of two grains. Below is just a suggestion, but keep spices the same because these bring the cleansing, nourishing, and rejuvenating process into balance. I have used it with clients to help them restore the health of their digestive system.

Preparation time: 2 hours (good for 1-2 days if refrigerated)

Serves: 5-6 people

INGREDIENTS

2 C. Basmati rice (white or brown). *May substitute medium grain brown rice or other white. White Basmati is easiest to assimilate but lacks fiber. Cook separate from beans.*

2 C. Green mung beans. *For variety, may use any bean. All dried beans are reconstituted.*

8-10 C. Water

1 T. Ghee (clarified butter). *May substitute olive oil. Check with physician.*

1 tsp. Ground cumin

1 tsp. Ground coriander

½- 1 tsp. Turmeric powder

1-2 tsp. Powdered ginger or fresh ginger

Unrefined sea salt

1 Clove garlic or onion *(optional)*

1 Sprinkle cayenne pepper

Pinch of Hing (asafoetida powder). This aids in protein assimilation *(optional)*

Add 2-3 C. Green leafy vegetables (collards, kale, Swiss chard, dandelion greens) plus onion or leek, and 2 carrots.

Choose vegetables that suit your constitution.

Acceptable legumes include green mung, yellow mung, aduki, green and red lentils, split peas. (My preference is green mung.)

Suggested grains are all rice varieties except standard white rice.

All spices may be substituted for others. The above list is just what has worked for my clients as well as me. This is for those who need to increase digestion and vitality while rebuilding the metabolism.

Alternative spices: Black peppercorns, cardamom, cayenne pepper, cinnamon, fennel, garlic, fresh ginger (minced), and mustard seeds (let mustard seeds pop in a ½ tsp. of hot oil).

Before the day of preparation: Soak beans in an uncovered pot for at least 12 hours before cooking. Best is 24 hours.

On the day of preparation: Measure 1 C. of rice and 1-1/2 C. of presoaked beans. (If using lentils, measure 1 C. dry. They don't need to be soaked prior to cooking). I like to use one part beans to one part rice, because we tend to eat too many starches. If you have digestive difficulties, increase the rice proportion while lowering the bean amount.

In a soup pot: Heat gently 1-2 T. of clarified butter (ghee) or olive oil. (If you don't have high cholesterol or triglycerides, you may use ghee.) While heating, add the cumin, coriander, turmeric, and asafoetida. Sauté these spices lightly in the ghee until they are just browned but before they blacken, and add the mung beans and rice, stirring for about a minute so some of the spices will be absorbed. Then add water, ginger, cayenne, and kombo (optional), a seaweed that softens the beans. Bring to a slow boil, cover, and cook until the individual grains are completely soft.

This recipe has been adapted slightly from classical Ayurvedic recipes. You can further adjust it to meet your personal needs.

Core Practices

The practices in this lesson continue to deepen our awareness at the abdominal region (hara), the place where we physically digest our food but also generate our core vitality and stamina. As we continue to work with the abdominal region, we begin to feel more strength and stability in our daily encounters. Our physical digestion also begins to show signs of strength and efficiency.

WORKING WITH THE PELVIC TILT (PHASE 2)

Purpose:

Gain awareness of the pelvic floor and abdominal muscles.

Technique:

1. Come onto the hands and knees with the hands shoulder width apart and the knees hip distance apart.

2. Gently, press the shin bones and top of the feet into the floor for stability.

3. Spread the fingers wide and press the palms into the floor.

4. Begin on an exhale and tuck the tail bone (coccyx) under, and contract the abdominal muscles toward the spine. Keep the upper body stable—it does not arch the full spine like in the yoga cat pose.

5. Next, inhale, lift the tailbone, and release the abdomen towards the floor as you feel your buttocks open and widen with the release. Here the pelvis tilts or rocks like in the reclining pelvic tilt that you did in the last lesson. Think of the belly filling like a balloon.

6. Repeat 5-7 times.

Note: *As you continue the practice over time, keep the pelvis stationary as you contract the pelvic floor in addition to the lower and upper abdomen. And when you release, just allow the belly to release and fill. This will give an added dimension to the lift, making it deeper and wider.*

ABDOMINAL SQUEEZE
AKUNCHANA PRASARANA

Purpose:

To gain awareness and access to the abdominal and pelvic muscles in a standing pose.

Technique:

1. Adopt a standing posture with the feet hip distance apart.

2. Lean forward with the knees bent slightly. You may have the buttocks leaning against the wall for stability.

3. Place the hands on the upper thighs where the arms can remain straight to support and rest the upper body.

4. Eyes can be opened or closed depending on your preference.

5. Tilt the chin forward to look at the naval or abdominal area.

6. Bring your awareness to the breath in the abdominal area.

7. Exhale, tuck the tail bone (coccyx) under, and contract the abdominal muscles toward the spine. Keep the upper body stable.

8. Inhale, lift the tailbone, and release the abdomen towards the floor as you feel the buttocks open and widen with the release. Again, here you can allow the pelvis to tilt with the contraction and roll back on release. Think of the belly filling like a balloon.

9. Repeat 5-7 times.

Note: *As you continue the practice over time, you can stabilize the pelvis so it doesn't move as you contract the pelvic floor, lower and upper abdomen. And the pelvis doesn't rock as you release the upper and lower abdomen, and pelvic floor.*

"The doctor of the future will give no medicine but will interest his patients in the care of the human frame —in diet and in the cause and prevention of disease."

—THOMAS EDISON

It's a Matter of Having the Guts to Be Happy

We've heard it from a discouraged person: "I don't have the stomach for this" or "I can't stomach this." Does it mean she thinks of her gut as the seat of courage, nerves of steel, and happiness? I doubt it. We use the language without consciously realizing that the healthier our gut, the more stable and strong is our nervous system.

Many traditional medical systems know the importance of the gut in maintaining our health and happiness. This lesson will shed light on what science has to say on the issue that was intuited centuries ago. Here we continue to explore the gut and move a little deeper into the understanding of how it communicates with our brain in a bidirectional manner. We continue with developing the practices to create a deeper awareness of the machinery that gives us the energy and immunity to focus and sustain our feeling good.

ON BALANCE, WE HAVE A VERY NERVOUS SYSTEM

Our bodies contain a Nervous System whose sole purpose is to maintain homeostasis for our organism. It's comprised of two branches: the Central Nervous System (CNS), which includes the brain and spinal cord, and the Peripheral Nervous System (PNS), which branches off into the Somatic and Autonomic nervous systems. There are two branches to the Autonomic Nervous System (ANS): the Sympathetic and the Parasympathetic Nervous Systems.

In our lesson on breath, we learned that our breathing is the only activity with both autonomic and somatic functions. The Enteric Nervous System (ENS) is part of the ANS, since it's influenced by the parasympathetic and sympathetic branches of the nervous system, including the vagal afferents that transmit information back to the brain from the ENS. However, due to its complexity, it's considered a separate nervous system because it doesn't need the brain to operate.

Keep in mind that the gut is regulated or influenced by both branches of the ANS, but within the gut walls an extensive system of nerve cells operate outside of the parasympathetic and sympathetic influence. It's known that these enteric plexus—the vast networks of nerve cells that extend throughout the entire gastrointestinal tract—can and do operate independently according to their own inner intelligence. As a result, these networks can monitor and facilitate many activities, both mechanical and chemical in nature.

The term "second brain" has been applied to the Enteric Nervous System because it has a mind of its own.[3] Embedded in the gastrointestinal tract, it houses more than 100 million neurons and is more wired than the CNS. It contains every class of neurotransmitters, the same as those found in the brain—acetylcholine, dopamine and serotonin, GABA, as well as others. It can operate on its own.

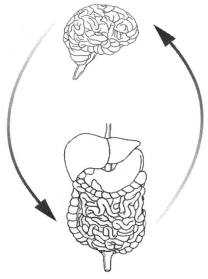

The ENS communicates with the CNS by way of endocrine function, immune responses, and the vagus nerve. One of the most interesting finds among modern scientists had been discovered by the ancient yogis many centuries earlier. The *vagus nerve*, translated as wandering nerve, is the parasympathetic nerve that serves as a major highway from the gut back to the brain. That explains ancient yoga therapeutic practices that focus on working with the health of the gut.

Other pathways that facilitate communication between the gut and the CNS take place by way of endocrine and immune pathways. For example, the gut can make its own version of neurotransmitters that affect the way we feel. It can even modulate our immune system.

There is much interest in these three mechanisms: neuronal, by way of the vagus nerve, endocrine, and immune pathways, and how they not only affect our brain function, but also our emotions and feelings. What sends these signals of communication? Blame it on the bacteria.

THE MICROBIOME GIVES BACTERIA A GOOD NAME

The human *microbiome* is the collective genes of all the bacteria that inhabit our entire human organism. Let's examine some numbers to appreciate the extensiveness of this microbiome. The bacteria inhabiting our gut are called the gut microbiome. Bacterial cells in the gut are quite numerous, about 100 trillion and probably more when all are identified. They actually outnumber our human genes by a factor of 100.[4]

The gut is fascinating for its ability to harbor its own world of resident bacteria. Popular association with bacteria isn't flattering. Let's agree it wouldn't be high on your list of bragging rights. So it's ironic that our bacterial genes keep us healthy and feeling good. These friendly bacteria actually help sustain our organism—us—in a healthy environment. When pathogenic bacteria invade our good bacteria, sickness results. What and how we eat, and how we think and feel, can injure and annihilate the good bacteria. That's when we become susceptible to illness.

Our gut microbiome is responsible for many functions that provide nourishment to our entire organism. In addition, it synthesizes vitamins and is the communication network to our brain. The biochemistry of our gut and our mind depends on the microbiota—the colonies of bacteria that inhabit our gut. Our diet and environment, as well as our thoughts, fears, and desires, affect these colonies, and that determines whether we feel anxious or calm, happy or depressed.

This finding is leading researchers to further investigate the microbiome for solutions to some of the issues related to depression, anxiety, overall mood, cognition, and inflammatory pain. Unfortunately, we frequently come to acknowledge our inner environment only when we're not feeling good.

Of continued concern is the way so many doctors treat symptoms instead of detecting ways to prevent the issue at hand. It's common thinking in the medical community that a mental disturbance is chronic and is resistant to change; that feeling out of sorts is a permanent condition; and that it's acceptable to identify with this condition.

The good news is that the field of neuroscience is now coming to recognize (what gastroenterology recognized long ago) that the microbial ecology of the gut indeed may influence our emotional and mental health[5]. A medical specialty with its foundation in the brain-gut relationship—enteric neuroscience—gives us reason to be optimistic. This marriage of gastroenterology and neuropsychiatry accepts that the gut contains a complex, vast network of neurons that communicate with the brain and work independently to regulate digestion.

Earlier than 1910, there is evidence of research linking the microbiome with health. The work of Elie Metchnikoff, a scientist known as the father of natural immunity, laid the foundation for some of the work we're seeing today with regard to the gut micro-biome and its relation to our physical and mental health.[6]

THIS IS OUR GUT CALLING OUR BRAIN

As we've discussed, our gut communicates with our brain via neuronal connections, such as the vagus nerve, endocrine connections, and immune modulators. This gut-and-brain conversation occurs in a loop or bidirectional manner. It's not a monologue coming only from the gut or only from the brain. [7]

Let's take a brief look at three proposed communication pathways used by gut bacteria to signal upward to the brain. The parasympathetic vagus nerve is stimulated during diaphragmatic breathing, so when we apply diaphragmatic breathing as our default breath, we continually send signals supporting relaxation.

A second communication pathway is by way of the cytokines and prostaglandins. These substances linked to the immune system act as hormonal regulators of the immune system. Cytokines are necessary to help us regulate inflammation and promote healing. Our microbiome in the gut contains immune cells—in fact, more immune cells than in the rest of the body. They stimulate the immune system to protect our organism when needed.

Remember that inflammation in the gut reflects inflammation in other parts of the body, especially the brain. The microbiome produces short chain fatty acids (SCFA) that are anti-inflammatory because they inhibit cytokine production. In addition, the microbiome protects the gut tissue from pathogens, increases blood flow and cell turnover, and helps lymphoid tissue to grow. This gut-associated lymphoid tissue, or GALT, helps us. Consider this: The gut is that part of our being that allows us to function in the outside environment, so it requires a protective layer. Some 60 percent of the lymphatic tissues surrounding the gut helps keep out foreign invaders.

The gut contains the largest amount of immune tissues in the body. These tissues are intertwined with nerve tissue outside the central nervous system, enabling the gut to communicate to the CNS what is happening outside of it. In turn, the CNS sends nerve impulses to help regulate homeostasis.

The last pathway from the gut worth mentioning is communication by way of the *hypothalamic pituitary axis* or HPA. This negative feedback loop connects the hypothalamus with the pituitary gland and our adrenals. Does this have the makings of a stress circuit? Most definitely yes.

You can affect your gut microbiota when stressed through negative thinking or with foods that cause inflammation, like genetically modified organisms, gluten, alcohol, antibiotics, harmful chemicals, and too many night shade vegetables, such as eggplants, peppers, tomatoes, and potatoes. (This inflammation would occur only in people genetically susceptible to allergies or unable to process food.)

As a result, the inflammation response is switched on, the immune signal is sent, and the stress response created, signaling the hypothalamus to produce a hormone called corticotrophin (CRH) that acts on the pituitary gland. Then the pituitary produces adrenocorticotropic hormone (ACTH) and tells the adrenal glands located above the kidneys to produce cortisol. In turn, cortisol signals back to the hypothalamus and pituitary to stop production. This process constitutes a negative feedback loop.

This simplified explanation illustrates how cortisol disrupts the integrity of the microbiota in the gut by creating openings in the protective barrier. In this state of "leaky gut," pathogens or harmful bacteria and proteins reach the interior of our organism through the openings, and that affects our entire physiology, especially our brain.

One additional important point: Stress is one of the major causes for our gut microbiome to become disturbed. Stress hormones lower a compound called *Brain-Derived Neurotropic Factor* (BDNF), a protein in the hippocampus, cortex, and other areas that is vital to learning, memory, and higher thinking. High BDNF is associated with positive mood and neuroprotection, and probiotics may increase the BDNF.[8]

This crash course in digestive science illustrates why the gut should be considered first when dealing with any type of stress-induced emotional or psychological issue. It's the gut microbiota that helps us come back to homeostasis after a stressful experience. Supplementing our diet with good, healthy prebiotic and probiotic foods makes our body more resilient when we encounter stress.

Mini Practice
THE INNER SMILE

ON RETREAT, I introduce an interesting, often misunderstood practice. When I first tell participants to practice the inner smile, they look at me and laugh almost in disbelief that I would suggest something so silly. That assumption is actually far from the truth. I learned of the inner smile when reading Mantak Chia's book, *Awakening Healing Energy through the Tao.*[9]

I never forgot this practice but made some modifications to support my entire microbiome. I share it here.

Sit or lie down in a comfortable position. Bring attention to your abdominal region, as you inhale and exhale using diaphragmatic breathing. Imagine each of the trillions of cells with smiles as they work to keep your body and mind in perfect harmony.

Use this any time you feel like you're falling into a dark abyss of negativity. It will send positive feedback to your microbiome colonies. Apply the practice to any part of your body where you experience difficulty. For example, envision your liver with a big smile. Positive intentions will produce a happy cell.

GET COMFORTABLE WITH
HOME-GROWN BACTERIA

Given their recent popularity, it could be a surprise to many that probiotics were discovered nearly 50 years ago, in 1965. People might not understand the extent to which probiotics improve their health and well-being, but many are becoming familiar with these digestive cultures. Partly responsible is the widely publicized benefit of supplementing with probiotics while completing a course of antibiotics.

Probiotics take their name from the Greek, "for life," an appropriate association because probiotics are the living cultures that, when ingested, help populate the already existing colonies. Prebiotics are precursors for the probiotic bacteria found in the colon. Because they're not digested in the small intestine, they travel unaffected to the colon where they serve as food (fermented substrates) for our bacterial colonies.

We're told to eat foods that are naturally swamped with probiotics, but what does this mean? These foods are grown in organic soils free of pesticides and chemicals. Bacteria are everywhere, and when we ingest foods we take in a host of them, some good but some not so good. If we choose foods from well-nourished soil, we'll be populating our organism with beneficial bacteria.

Don't forget that bacteria in our gut is local. What I mean by this is that our microbiota adapts to our environment, which is why our gut could have an issue when we travel abroad and eat the food. When we consume foods produced in our local environment, we support our microbiome with the same types of bacteria.

Eating clean, locally grown and prepared foods is a good way to keep our microbiota healthy and happy. This isn't to suggest that we shouldn't eat imported foods, but there needs to be a balance.

Researchers are hard at work determining the extent to which these substances benefit us beyond improved digestion. A 2013 study revealed that consuming probiotics can modulate brain activity. Thirty-six healthy women who exhibited no GI or psychiatric issues were divided into three test groups. The first consumed fermented yogurt containing several bacteria (bifidobacterium animalis subsp lactis, streptococcus thermophilus, lactobacillus bulgaricus, and lactococcus lactis subsp lactis) twice a day for four weeks.[10]

The second group, which served as a control, consumed non-fermented milk twice a day for four weeks, and the third group didn't consume any product over the duration of the four weeks. The results were derived from brain scans conducted when each woman was in a resting state and then was exposed to an emotional-reactivity task. After viewing pictures of faces showing emotions of anger and fear, each woman was asked to match them to other faces showing the same emotion. This task was designed so researchers could measure areas of the brain that process affective and cognitive functions when given a visual stimulus.

The findings reveal that those who consumed the probiotic mixture, when shown the pictures, had decreased activities in the insular and the somatosensory cortex, the areas of the brain that process emotions, cognition, and sensory input such as touch. Participants in the other two test groups either had no response or, in some cases, showed an increased activity in the stress-related centers in the brain when given the task of picture identification.

One other finding relevant to discovering the extent of the communication: Even at rest, the yogurt-eating group of women showed greater connectivity between the periaqueductal grey area of the brain stem and the prefrontal cortex involved in executive function (the set of mental functions, e.g., our ability to manage time and attention as well as integrating our experiences).

Including fermented foods in our diet is another way to feed our community of probiotics. How much, no one knows, but including some fermented foods can be beneficial since they already contain the live bacteria.

Fermented foods include miso, sauerkraut, kefir, yogurt, and anything else we want to ferment. The original source of food should be pesticide-free and organic.

We may hear claims that pesticides are beneficial because they prevent a plant from eliciting compounds (in response to being eaten by an insect) that are poisonous to us. I really don't buy into this thinking. I suspect such statements are funded by the chemical industry. I would think it far better to eat a leafy vegetable with a few worm holes rather than a vegetable that has been saturated with pesticides.

Choose foods that serve as prebiotics. These soluble fibers found in food plants basically serve as a fertilizer to our microbiota. They help stimulate and possibly activate growth of the bacteria colonies. From a biochemistry perspective, they include foods that contain naturally occurring inulin and fructo-oligosaccharides

(FOS). These stammer-inducing words are long-chained sugars that occur naturally in foods.

Pay attention here. The inulin that is added to commercial yogurt differs from the naturally occurring substance. When compounds are reproduced or extracted from their natural state, the biochemistry changes. For example, sugar cane isn't an enemy in its natural state but, when refined, it becomes too concentrated for our organism to handle.

Prebiotics can be found in leeks, bananas, onions, asparagus, Jerusalem artichokes, whole beans, whole grains, garlic, and even chicory. Some scientists believe prebiotics might be better for those with ailments that don't respond well to probiotics. In my experience, I would get prebiotics from natural foods rather than supplementing with prebiotic formulations. Natural constituents isolated by manufacturers don't behave the same way when they enter the human organism. This also holds true for herbs.

GUTTING OUR DIET

Now that we understand the importance of our gut in the way we feel, how can we eat to establish a new gut environment? First, we eliminate from our diet anything that could be causing a problem, like wheat gluten, chemicals, GMO (genetically modified organisms) foods, negative thinking, and stress.

We repair the damage by sealing the leaks that appear when the microbiota has been compromised. Glutamine, the most abundant amino acid in the body (helps build protein), and zinc help repair the gut lining. Probiotics and vitamins all feed the microbi-ota. For easily obtainable food sources that contain glutamine, we look to most cheeses, animal products, raw spinach, raw parsley, and cabbage.

We maintain flow by keeping our intestines moving. If we en-counter some pathogens, they'll be removed from the inner tube quickly and efficiently. In this case, herbal blends like triphala (an Ayurvedic formula consisting of three fruits used to cleanse and nourish the GI tract) are very good. Or, if we want more of a me-chanical process, we use psyllium husks, a soluble fiber.

So we can see that working with our diet to include foods that are organically grown and well-prepared, and ingesting them on a regular basis, can maintain healthy gut flora. Supplements also are good because they keep things moving through the intestine, eliminating the time for harmful bacteria to emit toxins.

Keep in mind it's not always easy to find appropriate food, es-pecially if work requires us to travel. We can prepare for travel. I always pack triphala and some ginger for those times when food might not be optimally healthy. And, of course, I practice what I call the inner smile. When we're happy and cheerful, our gut flora feels our vibration and operates without panic.

I've found that eating a "forbidden" food once in a while is a lot less harmful than having negative thoughts and emotions. If we imagine each of our molecules wearing a smile as it courses through our bloodstream, we could help our body remain healthy, even if our food choices aren't optimal for the day. Our gut feelings matter, too. So we keep a smile on our internal friends because they're here to serve us for the better.

In our next series of lessons, we work our way to the head, where our brain resides. We've learned that our gut microbiome communicates with the brain and vice versa, so now it's time to see the workings of our brain—what nourishes it and what keeps it functioning to help us maintain our ability to remain calm and focused.

Review

TRUTH

The health of our gut microbiome affects our happiness.

OBSTACLE

Physical & mental toxin bombardment in the environment.

EXIT STRATEGY

Restore our gut microbiome.

FACTS

❖ Bacteria in our gut are the gut microbiome.

❖ The gut has over 100 trillion bacterial cells.

❖ The gut bacteria exceed our human genes by a factor of 100.

❖ Restoring the microbiome can bring mental balance.

Path *of* Practice

"To keep the body in good health is a duty, for otherwise we shall not be able to trim the lamp of wisdom, and keep our mind strong and clear. Water surrounds the lotus flower, but does not wet its petals."

—BUDDHA

 JOURNAL ACTIVITY

Purpose:

To evaluate and record moods and energy level changes after including pre- and probiotic nutrients to your diet.

Technique:

1. Record your results from including pre- and probiotic nutrients in your diet.

2. Pay attention to how you feel (especially in the morning), how you sleep, your cravings and your appetite in general.

3. Notice if you feel less fatigued and more in balance.

4. Can you see a correlation between the gut and the brain? Have you developed the awareness that how, what, and when you eat affects your moods and emotions?

5. What foods make you feel light and cheerful? Which ones make you feel heavy and grumpy? Record your observations.

Core Practice

The core practices are an extension of those presented in Lessons 4 and 5. They revolve around gaining access and developing awareness in the pelvic/abdominal region. This practice combines all the elements into a powerful sequence that helps to collect, contain and circulate your vital energies. It is one of the most powerful skills to master.

AGNI SARA
(agni means "fire;"
sara means "essence")

Agni Sara literally means "energizing the solar system," but here the solar system refers to the interconnection of the psychological and physiological processes that control our physical and mental digestion.

Purpose:

Core foundation practice that, with consistency, will help massage internal organs and their associated chakras, resulting in cleansing and energizing the body and purifying the mind. Purification here is opening the energy channels by releasing stored impressions and associations that create emotional obstacles.

Technique:

1. Adopt a standing posture with the feet hip-distance apart, as above. You may have the butt against the wall for stability.

2. Lean forward with the hands placed on the upper thighs where the arms can remain straight to support and rest the upper body.

3. Bend the knees slightly. Eyes can be opened or closed, depending on your preference. Tilt the chin forward to look at the navel or abdominal area. Bring your awareness to the breath in the abdominal area.

4. On an exhale (think of this exhale like a wave), contract the pelvic floor as you squeeze and lift the lower belly and upper belly. Hold the squeeze and do a final lift, drawing the diaphragm muscle up under the ribs.

5. Immediately, release the lift and begin your inhalation while releasing in a wavelike motion the upper belly, lower, and finally the pelvic floor with the last inhalation. Try to keep the lower abdomen and pelvic floor contracted as you begin your inhalation.

6. Continue the process within your capacity without strain. If you lose your focus, stop and take a few breaths and try again. The focus is key here, because the mind will energetically do the lifting. You're working with the energy channels. (Refer to Lesson 10 on energy channels, if needed.)

7. Don't be concerned with the last step if you're not able to feel the diaphragm move up; just work with the wave motion without pauses or interruptions. Start with 5 and work up to 25.

Points

This is a master practice and is core to feeling good. It's best practiced in the morning after bowels are evacuated and no food has been taken in. Consistency is the key here, so make it a habit to practice this daily at least five times. Regulate the practice so it's a wavelike motion that requires total focus and control of the breath.

> **Note:** *The practice will teach you how to make fine-tuned adjustments to accommodate your physio-psycho matrix. For example, I prefer to have my entire foot turned slightly inward with my thighs also rotated inward about 5-10 degrees—ever so slight. This allows me to work on the energy channels that are weaker in my constitution. Each person is different, so trust what feels right for you.*

Counter-indications for all postures

Like many already described, don't do it if you suffer high blood pressure, heart problems, ulcers, hernias, pregnancy, menstruation, or any other condition that can cause an issue; e.g., women with IUD's may experience irritation.

"When diet is wrong, medicine is of no use.
When diet is correct, medicine is of no need."
—**A**YURVEDIC **P**ROVERB

LESSON 7

It's a Matter of Connection

We now move from discussion of the hara—the abdominal area—in which we spoke about the importance of our digestive system and microbiome, to the head, where our brain is housed. Our lesson offers a broad survey of nourishment for the brain, because only when it's properly fed can the brain serve the needs of our mind.

We've learned that a healthy gut supports a healthy brain and, conversely, a healthy brain serves to build a healthy gut microbiome. Now, on a purely physical level, we first will examine how carbohydrates fuel our brain's energy, how good fats support neuronal connections to insulate our brain, and how proteins (namely, our amino acids) serve as the foundation for connecting our entire brain.

We will learn that The Big 3—carbohydrates, fats, and proteins—although powerful, aren't enough to sustain us. Other nutrients are required to fortify us during the constant assault from stress, toxins, and the aging process. The micronutrients that fulfill that role will be revealed. Armed with this information, this lesson can serve as a guide to familiarize us with vitamins and minerals that help to protect the brain by enabling many biochemical processes to take place. They are the energy catalysts that keep it flowing uninterrupted.

EATING WITH OUR BRAIN IN MIND

We would love our brains to serve us well, and for as long as possible. We cringe with trepidation at words like dementia, stroke, Alzheimer's, or Parkinson's diseases and wish we could remove them from our vocabulary. This lesson is full of practical advice on ways to keep our brains healthy and agile using the basic nutrients in our day-to-day meals.

Are there days when your mind seemed foggy or lethargic although you slept well and didn't have many demanding tasks? Did you blame it on the weather or view it as a seasonal or age thing? Did it ever occur to you that the problem might have been what you ate that day?

We have high expectations of the power of our brain to boost mood and enhance mental clarity, but do we know what's required for the brain to feel good most of the time? There's much speculation on this subject; however, it's clear that foundation macro- and micronutrients influence the functionality of this organ, together with some herbs that rejuvenate the brain, and ultimately rejuvenate the mind. The chemistry of herbs and their use is a vast subject and beyond the scope of this lesson.

We use our body as feedback because it's far easier to address the physical part of ourselves (the brain) than the subtle realms of the mind field. Throughout the lessons of this book, we've used the body as feedback by incorporating practices and journaling that help us gain awareness to our physical and psychological functioning. Now let's examine the basic physical nutrients for the brain and how these nutrients support and sustain a calm and focused mind with the resilience needed during difficulties.

A properly nourished brain will serve our entire organism in times of change, for example, during the hormonal fluctuations of menarche and menopause, or when we're called upon to have more focus to perform our daily duties, or even to remain calm when facing a stressful event. This is why, in the long run, we must live with the nourishment of our brain in mind.

THE GREAT CARB DEBATE IS A DRAW

Controversy about carbohydrates is raging. Do they age the brain? Do they make us fat? The list of purported ills grows on. The claim that carbohydrates cause inflammation is partially true, but we must look at the whole picture and not listen to the propaganda.

From my perspective as a nutritional biochemist, I can state that carbohydrates cause inflammation for a variety of reasons. First, they're laced with chemicals that destroy and inflame healthy tissues, including the brain. Second, grains that have been modified (for example, changing the gluten in wheat) produce a new material that human and non-human organisms can't assimilate or use. The body reacts appropriately, creating an inflammatory response or even an autoimmune response in which the organism's own cells attack themselves. Third, our digestive system becomes inflamed and can't properly digest the carbohydrates.

The best-known macronutrients—carbohydrates from grains, fruits, vegetables, and dairy products—are the most widely consumed foods. Their sugar breaks down to glucose, the brain's most preferred form of fuel, possibly because it's the major energy source in the blood.

The brain's energy requirement is greater than for other organs, owing to its massive energy expenditure through electrical signaling and its inability to store fat or glucose.[11] Carbohydrates provide the quickest form of energy for the brain in the form of glucose, a 6-carbon sugar that assists with memory and concentration and is used during times of stress-related anxiety or panic.

Glucose is metabolized from those carbohydrates in our diet that are produced by photosynthesis. In this solar-fueled process, plants manufacture their own food with water absorbed by their roots and carbon dioxide drawn from the air. The chemical that makes this possible is *chlorophyll*, which gives that green color to the vegetables we eat and the plants we grow. The net result is a carbohydrate.

Carbohydrates consumed in a meal or snack are digested and broken down into glucose, which is delivered to the brain, nervous system, and other cells within our bodies. Glucose is used as fuel to keep the metabolism furnaces burning. Stored mainly in the liver for use between meals, it is also used internally by muscles. As we learned earlier, the brain feeds on glucose but doesn't store it, so the role of glucose when we feel fatigued or anxious cannot be denied.

Our ability to focus and think clearly is related to blood glucose concentration. The brain thinks well when it has food, and since the glucose it derives from carbohydrates is its food, optimal blood sugar is important. Studies show that glucose is necessary for production of acetylcholine, a brain neurotransmitter required for memory.[12] Glucose is responsible for all the neurotransmitter production, which requires expenditure of brain energy.

The ability to think isn't the only brain process affected; all areas of the brain need sugar. If our sugar level is off, our mood will change. People with low blood sugar are usually irritable, anxious, or even depressed. Once they eat and replace their blood sugars, their mood will improve dramatically. Weight-loss dieting can often cause fluctuations in blood sugar, which may manifest in moodiness, as many of us might have experienced firsthand. If our glucose levels fluctuate too much, we may experience mental confusion, dizziness, fatigue, and, in severe cases, convulsions and loss of consciousness.

How does this occur? Stress-related anxiety and depression are the plague of modern life. People are literally suffering from impairment of glucose metabolism through prolonged stress that manifests itself as anxiety, depression, and even attention disorders that prevent a person from remaining calm. This has been evident to me when working with clients who are overworked and have exhausted their brain fuels. When the body experiences stress caused by undernourishment (such as being overworked and overburdened with worry and negative emotions), the brain signals the body to go into danger mode.

Over time, the adrenal glands that are responsible for maintaining our homeostasis become depleted and are unable to maintain the balance. That's when we experience symptoms of anxiety and even fear. I make it a priority to help clients restore their adrenal reserves through the proper intake of carbohydrates, herbal preparations, and homeopathic remedies, if needed. Adrenal recovery can require from 6-8 weeks, but good results appear within the first week.

HERE'S THE LOWDOWN ON SUGAR HIGHS

As we know, the highly refined, highly processed "junk sugars" found in candy, icings, syrups, packaged baked goods, and table sugar cause the greatest fluctuation in blood sugar. These have the most remarkable effect on our moods and energy levels. While food or drink can give us a quick boost, it's quite short-lived. And that describes about 90 percent of everything we see on the shelves of a standard supermarket.

Not all carbohydrates are equal. A simple carbohydrate, namely refined table sugar, isn't the same as the complex carbohydrate we derive from whole grains because each metabolizes differently and produces a specific effect on the brain. For example, when we ingest sucrose in the form of pastries or frosted cereals, it breaks down into glucose and fructose. If you think, "Glucose and fructose are natural, so we're getting good sugar," you're wrong. Keep in mind that the metabolic breakdown of this compound uses a lot of energy, depleting vitamins and minerals in its conversion. When we eat a whole grain or whole food, less energy is expended in the breakdown because the process uses nutrients that are contained in the food being consumed, thus, having less demand on the system.

Blood sugar is regulated by insulin, a hormone secreted from the pancreas. Refined carbohydrates overwork the pancreas and deplete insulin. Depending on a person's genetic programming, disease can result.

Let's look at this in more detail. Simple sugars are used rapidly; when gone, blood sugar plunges to a sugar low. Low blood sugar triggers the release of adrenal hormones (as occurs when we're stressed by a thought), which signals the liver to deliver stored sugar, and that again elevates blood sugar levels. This is the science behind what is innocuously termed a "sugar high." In reality, the blood sugar roller coaster affects mood and concentration in children and adults as they experience not only those sugar highs, but also the "sugar blues."

The ups and downs of blood sugar and adrenal hormones can stimulate neurotransmitter imbalance, leading us to fidget, feel irritable, be inattentive, feel inexplicably sleepy, or suffer a troubling anxiety attack. On the descent of a blood sugar roller coaster, the glucose available to the brain has dropped precipitously. Neurons, unable to store glucose, experience an energy crisis. After the up-ward rush, we feel spaced-out, weak, confused, and nervous. Our ability to focus and think is compromised.

⁓

FAT CHANCE

Fat just might be the most debated, misunderstood, and vilified dietary element in this early part of the 21st century. Difficult as this might be to believe, most of us don't get the fat we need from an average diet. We consume more than enough fat—over the rec-ommended 20% of this second macronutrient—but it's not the right kind. Our bodies need *Essential Fatty Acids* (EFAs) but can't make them, so we have to supplement these EFAs through diet.

The brain contains a high concentration of fatty acids: Sub-tract water, and your brain is 60% fat (about 20% dry weight). In comparison, our other organs fall into the 6-20% range. Fats in the form of fatty acids protect neurons in the brain to allow proper signaling. If the right fats are so important, what's "adequate" and what's "optimal"?

For answers, let's embark on a brief biochemistry preview. EFAs are long-chain polyunsaturated fats, grouped into two fami-lies: omega-6 (*linoleic acid*) and omega-3 (*alpha linoleic acid*). Seemingly minor differences in their molecular structure make the two EFA families act very differently in the body. While the metabolic products of omega-6 fatty acids promote inflammation, blood clotting, and tumor growth, the omega-3 fatty acids act en-tirely opposite.

We need both omega-3s and omega-6s, but it's becoming increasingly clear that an excess of omega-6 fatty acids can have negative consequences. Many scientists believe the fatty acid ratios play a significant role in the high incidence of heart disease, hypertension, diabetes, obesity, premature aging, psychiatric disorders, and some forms of cancer. They point to the profound imbalance between our intake of omega-6 and omega-3 fatty acids.[13]

A comment here about our memory enhancers: The phospholipids, like the omega-3 fatty acids, are important for optimal brain function. These intelligent fats in the brain are a major component of biological membranes. As such, they play a vital role in the cell-signaling systems in the brain's neurons. As the name implies, phospholipids are made of a combination of lipids (fats) and the mineral phosphorous. Phospholipids are found in high concentrations in the lining of practically every cell of the body, including brain cells where they influence how well receptors function. Although present in many foods, highest concentrations of phospholipids are derived from soy, eggs, and the brain tissue of animals.

It's easy to understand why our brains need essential fatty acids. The brain cells that communicate with each other—neurons—are protected by a membrane, called *myelin*, which is predominantly comprised of fatty acid molecules. Research shows that altering dietary fat intake affects the fatty acid composition of brain cell membranes—namely the receptor sites—and leads to changes in a wide variety of cognitive function. A study on the aging brain reported that adult consumption of omega-3s increases grey matter brain volume. It also found evidence of new tissue development in the cortico-limbic (anterior cingulate cortex, amygdala and hippocampus) area of the brain associated with happiness.[14]

Fad and extreme diets, contemporary agribusiness and food-processing practices, and the pace of modern life that makes fast, take-out, and packaged foods hard to avoid all contribute to our current state of imbalance. An imbalance in omega-6 and omega-3 fatty acids and rampant omega-3 deficiency aren't just in our bodies—they're in our markets and on our menus. But this doesn't mean we can't tip the scales back toward equilibrium.

TRANS FAT DANGER CLEAR IN ANY LANGUAGE

Fats are basic building blocks of the brain, so eating trans fats blocks the energy channels, both physically and more subtly. It has become common knowledge that trans fats—found in anything with "hydrogenated" or "partially hydrogenated oil"—are weak and even dangerous construction materials because the way they are manufactured alters them molecularly. Normal fatty acids have a natural curve or kink to their molecular shape. Hydrogenation and deep frying mutate this, creating molecules that are more straight and narrow. These altered fat molecules fit more tightly together into cell membranes, making them more saturated and rigid, also preventing proper flexibility and function.

The cell membrane that protects our neurons, called myelin, is made up mostly of fatty acid molecules. Trans fatty acids can be incorporated into these crucial membranes and affect neuron activity. They impair the ability of neurons to communicate and likely cause degeneration and diminished mental performance. Neurodegenerative disorders like Parkinson's and Alzheimer's appear to feature decreased fatty acids in membranes. Eating trans fats also increases the risk of coronary heart disease.[15]

Health authorities worldwide recommend that consumption of trans fats be reduced to trace amounts. Trans fats from partially hydrogenated oils are generally considered to be more of a health risk than those occurring naturally.[16] Various legislative and voluntary bans on trans fats are going into effect around the world, but we don't have to wait for someone else to eliminate them. Let's banish them from our diet now.

PROTEIN GOES RIGHT TO YOUR HEAD

Protein is the third important macronutrient. Dietary proteins are the raw materials that supply amino acids, which are eventually converted to neurotransmitters, and this makes proteins essential for neuronal communication. Adequate, regular intake of quality protein is critical because, unlike carbohydrates and fats, amino acids—the building blocks of protein—aren't stored in the body. I say "quality" protein because, as with the other macronutrients, it pays to be selective. The detrimental effects of environmental pollution and agribusiness practices are seen in foods with high protein concentration, such as meat and fish. The high concentration of toxins ultimately disturbs the health of the organism.

The protein available in beans, vegetables, and whole grains is a better bet for the bulk of our protein needs. These sources provide protein when pulses are combined with grains, in addition to fiber, fats, carbohydrates, and micronutrients. Nuts, for example, a great source of protein, also contain unsaturated fat, including omega-3 that has a positive effect on cholesterol levels.

For the purpose of this lesson, when we talk about protein and the brain, we're talking about neurotransmitters—the messengers that relay signals from one brain cell to another—our connectors. Most neurotransmitters are made from amino acids obtained from dietary protein.

Neurotransmitters can't deliver their messages just anywhere. Like puzzle pieces, they need a precise fit in a receptor. Brain receptors have an exposed, cup-shaped end designed to fit mirror-imaged neurotransmitter molecules. (*Note: The receptors are dependent on fatty acids.*) Neurotransmitter "puzzle pieces" clicking into the appropriate receptors trigger a series of changes in the receptors that ultimately prompt a reaction in the cell body.

Many natural compounds and medicines mimic the molecule that we're trying to use and lock into the receptor sites. This is how addictive substances work in the brain; their size and shape is close to natural neurotransmitters. In the right amount or dose, these substances lock into receptors in the brain and start an unnatural chain reaction of electrical charges, causing neurons to release large amounts of their own neurotransmitter. Most addictive substances act upon dopamine receptors that signal pleasure.

Some substances lock onto the neuron and act like a pump, so the neuron releases more neurotransmitter. Other substances block reabsorption or reuptake and cause unnatural floods of neurotransmitter. All drugs of abuse, such as nicotine, cocaine, and marijuana primarily affect areas in the brain, in what scientists call the reward system. Normally, these reward centers respond to pleasurable experiences by releasing the neurotransmitter dopamine to create feelings of pleasure.

The most intense experience occurs when a person takes a drug for the first time. In the case of amphetamine, for instance, the limbic system is flooded with dopamine, but after the first dose the brain immediately begins to change in response to the unnatural rush of neurotransmitters. With this flooding of dopamine (in the case of cocaine or amphetamine), neurons start to reduce the number of dopamine receptors, and neurons may also reduce dopamine production. The result is less dopamine in the brain and what is called "down regulation." Because some drugs are toxic, some neurons may die.

So, when helping people wean from prescription or non-prescription drugs, it's necessary to supplement with the right nutrients to bring nourishment back to the brain to support the receptors. Over time, the receptors are nourished and balance is restored.

Our knowledge is growing as the result of active studies related to neurotransmitter function. As varieties of neurotransmitters in the brain are identified, their influence on behaviors is being understood. Neurotransmitter imbalance is being recognized in brain disorders such as Parkinson's disease, depression, and anxiety, as well as attention-deficit and obsessive-compulsive behaviors.

Early studies have shown that the number of receptors declines with age. For example, the neurotransmitter serotonin has been implicated in aging, showing alterations in both functional and structural capacities.[17-18] A similar age-related diminishment has been observed in our receptors for the neurotransmitter dopamine.[19] It has been proposed to result in a decline in cognitive and motor function. (Think "senior moment.") With proper nourishment and the right activity for the brain, however, these changes don't have to be a "normal" part of aging.

WHAT IS IT, WHY SHOULD WE CARE, AND WHAT SHOULD WE DO?

The names of some amino acids and neurotransmitters may be familiar because the signals they send are so well-known. The amino acid *tryptophan* in turkey makes us joke about falling asleep on the couch after a Thanksgiving meal. The same amino acid in milk makes us turn to a warm glass as a sleep aid. And the neurotransmitter *serotonin* is the second "s" in the currently popular SSRI (selective serotonin re-uptake inhibitor) family of antidepressant medications. These examples demonstrate that amino acids and neurotransmitters can be powerfully calming or energizing, which makes adequate, quality protein consumption all the more crucial.

Some amino acids are essential because they must be obtained from the diet, while others aren't because the body can manufacture them. The essential tryptophan and non-essential tyrosine are vital because of their influence over four primary neurotransmitters: serotonin (derived from tryptophan), dopamine, epinephrine, and norepinephrine (made from tyrosine).[20] Serotonin calms; the other three neurotransmitters energize. As described, SSRI drugs like Prozac work by increasing the brain's serotonin levels.

Meals that combine high protein (high in tyrosine) foods with low carbohydrates prompt the production of norepinephrine and dopamine, which perks us up with energy and alertness. We can see why a meal like this might be best at breakfast or midday when we need to present a talk or concentrate on a work project. High carbohydrate, low protein meals can increase the brain's tryptophan levels—and serotonin levels—leading to calm, contentment, and sleep. A carbohydrate-rich meal then might be appropriate at the end of the day, or for those suffering from sleeplessness due to anxiety.

While emotional and behavioral issues can indicate a brain inadequately nourished in amino acids, the brain also quickly absorbs and makes use of good nutrition. Because the brain is so responsive to what we eat, and because supplementation with isolated amino acids is poorly understood, it's advisable to get the amino acids we need from food. A variety of protein sources helps insure we derive the full range of necessary amino acids.

In terms of modulating mood and energy levels, you can be your own researcher. Try eggs one morning, toast the next, and observe your energy level. Compare the effects of pasta at midday or in the evening. See what works for your schedule—and your brain. *(Note: Eggs are high in choline, the precursor of acetylcholine, which plays a role in memory consolidation.)*

Protein and other nutrients in food are most accurately described as neurotransmitter precursors. Exactly how and the number of neurotransmitters produced from these precursors is an evolving area of study, one complicated by the fact that most foods contain more than one nutrient, and nutrient interactions affect the production and release of neurotransmitters. But in an effort to understand what kinds of protein we should consume—to get the amino acids and neurotransmitters our brains need—let's look at what we do know.

It's a wonder that **amino acids** reach our brain at all. Not only do brain cells compete with body cells for amino acids (body cells pull amino acids from the bloodstream more easily), but amino acids must also pass the protective blood-brain barrier. The blood-brain barrier is a membranic structure that acts primarily to protect the brain from chemicals in the blood, while not impeding essential metabolic function. It's composed of endothelial cells packed very tightly in brain capillaries. This higher density restricts passage of substances from the bloodstream much more than endothelial cells in capillaries elsewhere in the body.

And as if that were not restrictive enough, amino acids must be escorted through the blood-brain barrier by a certain molecule on a certain pathway in a certain "vehicle." For these reasons, when we eat protein and carbohydrates together, tryptophan wins the race and we have serotonin. Eat protein alone and tyrosine wins, giving us dopamine, norepinephrine, and epinephrine, since they share a pathway. This simplified explanation should illustrate why it pays to understand the rules of the road for amino acids.

Complete proteins (most animal sources, such as fish and

meat, fowl and eggs, cheese and yogurt) contain all the amino acids necessary to build protein. Not so with incomplete proteins (from fruits and vegetables, grains, legumes, seeds, and nuts). Incomplete proteins aren't inferior, but vegetarians and vegans need to be conscientious about eating a variety of protein-rich foods daily and combining them in ways that provide all needed amino acids. Traditional dietary practices have evolved to do this. For example, rice and beans, two proteins incomplete on their own, combine to make a complete protein.

The role of neurotransmitters is not widely understood by people who aren't in scientific circles; however, our discussions in this lesson highlight why anyone who wants to promote dietary change for feeling good must become well-versed in the science of nutrition. What follows is an at-a-glance primer of key neurotransmitters.

Dopamine is necessary for motivation, assertiveness, immune and nervous system function, and sexual arousal. Low levels and impaired ability to synthesize are related to age, Parkinson's disease, and attention-deficit disorder.

Norepinephrine is necessary for concentration, alertness, and motivation. It has adrenaline-like effects and is crucial for memory storage and optimal metabolism.

Serotonin is necessary for a sense of calm, contentment, well-being, and normal sleep. It helps regulate memory, learning, blood pressure, appetite, and body temperature. Low levels are connected to depression, insomnia, aggressive behavior, obsessive-compulsive behaviors, and sensitivity to pain.

Acetylcholine is necessary for thought and memory processes, muscular coordination, and concentration.

Gamma-Aminobutyric Acid or GABA is necessary for rest and relaxation. It inhibits pain and fear. Because it tells the brain to be quiet, malfunctioning GABA could play a role in most mood issues.

MICRONUTRIENTS ARE NOT OF LITTLE IMPORTANCE

We've seen how our brains are nourished by the macronutrients—carbohydrates, fat, and protein—but adequate intake of the Big 3 is not enough to sustain us. There are other nutrients our bodies need, especially because we're under constant assault from stress, toxins, and artificial food. Micronutrients fill that role. This part of the lesson serves as a guide to familiarize us with vitamins and minerals that help to protect the brain by enabling many biochemical processes to take place. They are the energy catalysts that keep it flowing uninterrupted.

Breath is sometimes used as a metaphor for life itself. While we no longer dangle and spank a newborn to elicit a cry, we do wait to hear that first sound as a sign that the baby is well and able to breathe. Indeed, oxygen makes life possible. Each of our billions of brain cells uses oxygen to stoke the fires of consciousness. The brain uses approximately 20% of the body's oxygen.[21] Although we need oxygen to survive, the oxygen *radical* (ROS), a normal by-product of oxygen metabolism, when in excess, can cause inflammation and erode the very structure of those brain cells.[22]

Micronutrients maintain the oxygen balance in the brain. They help beneficial oxygen reach it while combating the highly reactive forms of oxygen called *free radicals* that cause inflammation. Free radical production is a normal part of living and aging, but when in excess due to environmental insults, the process creates chemical reactions that damage brain cells. When free radicals are out of control, cells are damaged faster than they can be repaired. Think of these free radical reactions as a biological form of rust that erodes and infiltrates. It ages us by setting up disease states and diminishing brain function.

Our bodies have their own ability for dealing with free radicals. Much as a healthy immune system fends off viruses, antioxidants (anti-oxygen) counteract these oxidants. As we age, our natural antioxidants diminish, and the brain is an organ particularly vulnerable to such change. So it's important to eat highly nutritious foods and take a good multivitamin/mineral supplement.

Antioxidant vitamins (e.g., vitamins C and E) and micronutrients that contribute to antioxidant defenses (e.g., selenium) are protective for brain function support.

Because of the high energy demands of neurons in the brain, it's important for us to support its health with antioxidants, like coenzyme Q10 and glutathione, and many phytochemicals, like carotenes—crucial protectors for our brain cells. Antioxidants battle the free radicals linked to many brain diseases associated with aging, such as Alzheimer's. Numerous studies support the hypothesized role of free radicals in oxidative brain aging (memory loss, dementia, plaque formation) and in degenerative diseases, such as Alzheimer's, Parkinson's and vascular dementia.[23-28]

SMALL BUT ESSENTIAL ELEMENTS

This leads us to the micronutrients, of which there are 13 essential vitamins, about 7 major minerals, and 11 trace minerals. Vitamins and minerals serve as co-enzymes in our general metabolism; however, here we focus on the brain. While acknowledging that, in fruits and vegetables, the whole is in some ways greater than the sum of the parts, some plant food "parts" stand out. These vitamins and minerals have been studied. Some have been deemed beneficial in amounts not easily obtained in one's diet. For some, the optimal anti-aging and disease-fighting dose is unknown.

Here we briefly survey the well-studied heavy hitters among the valuable vitamin, mineral, and botanical micronutrients that support our well-being.

Vitamin A regulates cell growth and division. Beta carotene is a precursor of vitamin A.

Vitamin C is highly concentrated in the fluid around brain neurons—up to 100 times higher than elsewhere in the body. It protects DNA and other cell components and is crucial to the synthesis of the neurotransmitters dopamine and norepinephrine.

Vitamin E is a superb rejuvenating agent and the primary fat-soluble antioxidant for the brain, which has a heavy fat composition. This vitamin protects fatty acids from free radical damage, strengthens cerebral capillaries, helps make more oxygen available to the brain, and works to insure proper blood clotting, which has implications in stroke prevention.

Carotenoids include lutein, lycopene, beta carotene, alpha carotene, beta cryptoxanthin, and zeaxanthin. Alpha-carotene, found in many of the same foods as beta carotene, may well be an even more valuable antioxidant. Lycopene, the red pigment in tomatoes, is linked to low rates of cancer in those who consume the most.

Selenium is an essential trace mineral that works synergistically with vitamin E. It's a necessary component in several antioxidant enzymes the body makes to fight free radicals. It also detoxifies brain-damaging heavy metals, including mercury, lead, arsenic, and cadmium.

B vitamins are part of all reactions involving the nervous system and are powerful rejuvenating substances. Both norepinephrine and dopamine are manufactured from the amino acids, such as tyrosine or phenylalanine. This biochemical reaction occurs in the presence of adequate oxygen, but vitamins B3, B6 and C, folic acid, iron, and copper are also involved. Adequate intake of the B vitamins is required for these conversions to occur.

B1 (thiamin) converts glucose into brain energy and is required to create myelin, the insulation around nerve fibers that allows for efficient nervous system communication.

Folic acid (also a B vitamin), vitamin B6 (pyridoxine), and vitamin B12 (cobalamin) are being actively researched because of their effect on lowering homocysteine levels, where high levels of homocysteine are associated with heart disease and stroke.

B1(thiamin), B3 (niacin), B6 (pyridoxine), and folic acid help in the conversion of tryptophan to serotonin, the calming neurotransmitter.

GABA (gamma-aminobutyric acid) is associated with anxiety-related issues and uses B6 (pyridoxal phosphate) for its conversion of glutamate to the amino acid gamma- aminobutyric acid.

Magnesium is used in over 300 critical biochemical enzymatic reactions. It activates an enzyme in cell membranes that controls our balance of sodium and potassium, which is crucial to cell viability and function. Magnesium activates most of the enzymes crucial to cerebral metabolism and cognitive function.

I've found that using vitamins and minerals, along with a complete diet, helps improve mood and cognition. However, they're most effective with a healthy digestive system and good diet. It's essential to build our brain from the bottom up, restoring digestive function and nourishing the brain. When these two criteria are met, we can see the benefit to working deeper with our nourishment and bring awareness to how we feed our mind. This is the subject of our next lesson.

Review

TRUTH
All brains require all nutrients for optimal function.

OBSTACLES
An undernourished brain with unbalanced food intake.

EXIT STRATEGY
Focus on the brain-friendly diet.

FACTS

❖ The brain lacks energy storage and needs daily nutrients.

❖ Fats support & insulate for nerve transmission.

❖ Carbohydrates fuel the brain by supplying glucose.

❖ Amino acids help the brain to communicate.

Path *of* Practice

"Health is a state of complete harmony of the body, mind and spirit. When one is free from physical disabilities and mental distractions, the gates of the soul open."

—B.K.S. IYENGAR

 JOURNAL ACTIVITY

Purpose:

To evaluate and record moods and energy-level changes as you add the new diet habits presented below.

Technique:

1. Record the observations of how your mind/body complex tries to adjust while incorporating your dietary nutrient changes. For example, notice if you become less irritable and more mentally uplifted after eliminating wheat from your diet.

2. Assess if you're more energetic when you ingest fresh juice versus processed juice.

3. Assess your mental stability when adding essential fatty acids. The fatty acids will take a bit more time to have an effect, so give it at least six weeks.

Core Practice

MACRO MEAL PLAN

Plan your meals according to how you use your brain. A low-calorie, high-protein meal that also contains complex carbohydrates makes you more alert and would be perfect for breakfast and lunch for most people. A higher calorie, higher carbohydrate, lower protein meal could help you relax and fall asleep in the evening. If you have work or learning to do in the afternoon, don't end your midday meal with dessert. Experiment and observe your results.

Technique:

1. Eat a meal that allows tyrosine to enter the brain to perk you up. This meal should contain good quality protein, like eggs or fish, along with a minimum of carbohydrates so that insulin doesn't spike and push out the tyrosine. A meal like this would be a triple-egg white omelet with melted cheese, spinach, and mushrooms. After eating this kind of meal, do you feel alert, energized, "perked up"?

2. Eat a meal that allows tryptophan to enter the brain. This means you should have access to some carbohydrates so that insulin will be released, giving the tryptophan the right of way and the other amino acids a roadblock. A meal like this would be turkey with rice and dressing, a baked potato, and some

mixed green veggies. You needn't overindulge to make this kind of meal extremely high-caloric, but you must emphasize carbohydrates. Now do you feel calm and relaxed, perhaps even sedated?

3. Because calorie/carbohydrate/protein balances in meals affect different people in different ways, keep a diary of what you eat normally for a few days, noting not just what you eat, but also how you feel immediately and a few hours after each meal. Use this information to adjust your meals according to your performance needs. (*A diary of a school-age child's diet can be instructive for parents when trying to determine what foods enhance and hinder attention and performance.*)

"In this plate of food, I see
the entire universe
supporting my existence."
—A Zen Blessing

"The intuitive mind is a sacred gift and the rational mind is a faithful servant. We have created a society that honors the servant and has forgotten the gift."
—ALBERT EINSTEIN

It's a Matter of Thought

In the previous lessons, we explored physical aspects of what we feed our brain. When talking about the mind, we must consider food's subtle qualities. Food in the form of physical and subtle impressions has a direct impact on our consciousness, our feelings, and our emotions. These qualities to which I'm referring have an impact on the deepest part of our consciousness. If not properly addressed and understood, we can find ourselves traveling south when we're due north.

In this lesson, we'll look at the innate qualities of all of nature and the elements, and their influence on how we think and feel. In our discovery, we'll be able to recognize our psychological patterns and how we can influence these patterns by addressing what we feed our mind.

MAKE NURTURING CHOICES

Our life depends on nourishment from food, most of which has been alive as a plant or animal. The need for food makes pursuit of it a dominant activity for the animal and plant kingdoms. Most plants feed on water, sunlight, and nutrients from the soil or water. Animals consume plants and some other animals. Humans are practically omnivorous and in this century have shown an appetite not only for fast foods, but also for those foods containing or possibly being made totally from artificial, genetically modified organisms (GMO).

The purpose of food is to feed and nurture every cell in our body, so when we consume or take in vital foods, then our consciousness becomes calm, focused, and vital. On the other hand, when we use pre-fab foods or those that have been adulterated with pesticides and genetic manipulation to satisfy our need for nourishment, our consciousness gets confused and suffers from devitalization. We also feed our selves with things that aren't traditionally considered food, such as our thoughts, impressions, and experiences. Doesn't this count as food? Since everything we feed our selves ultimately becomes our consciousness, we can say, "yes." And if we want to have a healthy mind, we have to be vigilant about what we feed it.

We continually think about how we cleanse and nourish our body and must do the same for our mind. These things matter: How much food we need to live; what types of foods we eat; and what drives our appetites for the foods we choose. At some point in your life, you'll consider what you need to feed your body, but until you encounter a crisis, you probably won't take the time to look at what you feed your mind. And the odds are, what you learn will be ignored.

As the body needs food to be healthy, so does the mind. As the body benefits from fasting from food and exercise, so the mind should refrain from stimuli and exercise, using mantra and concentration practices.

The colors, shapes, smells, and sounds around us are the subtle elements that feed our mind. Our senses and our perception of the sensory stimuli affect the outer mind or *manas*, as well as the inner mind, *chitta*, or deeper consciousness. We will talk about this in the next lesson.

"The greatest force is derived from the power of thought.
The finer the element, the more powerful it is.
The silent power of thought influences
people even at a distance, because
mind is one as well as many.
The universe is a cobweb; minds are spiders."
—SWAMI VIVEKANANDA

Our mind is influenced by our lifestyle habits. For example, how much time you devote to the laptop, mobile devices, and television on a daily basis directly affects your mind. Do you spend time outdoors in nature, walking and experiencing the sensory impressions of the surrounding environment? Or do you function in an enclosed area, rarely taking the time to be outdoors and in tune with nature?

WE'RE WIRED FOR LIFE

There's an alarming trend among the younger generation to form relationships with and through their electronic devices instead of concentrating on real human interaction. Evidence of this unrelenting reliance on "remaining connected" is as near as a restaurant, where you'll find people fixated on their handheld devices while eating. What outcome can we expect from these habits? Perhaps it's a mind field that only can process sound bites and is unable to expand. While the modern mind field is fast and quick to respond, it lacks endurance, sustainability, focus, and calmness—resulting in what is termed "stress."

Quick-access, at-a-distance technology is rapidly replacing what used to be in-person human communication and relationships, with high value placed on types of social media. How ironic to remove personal interaction from communication that not only uses words but also "sounds, signs, or behaviors to express or exchange information or to express ideas, thoughts, or feelings to someone else."[29]

Should we be concerned that the effect of impersonal communication could be a human race confused by the lost connection with the source of inner knowledge? The mind is an instrument that is a reflection of what it's fed. Feed quality and you create quality. Feed junk food and you produce confusion, disturbance, stupefaction, and distraction. We could lose our capacity to know real from unreal, light from dark, truth from non-truth.

Here's a simple but unlikely solution to stem this alarming trend: Shun social media via electronic devices like smart phones, tablets, and computers. A realistic solution is first to recognize the distracted and disturbed mind, then what's creating it. You'll find that a glut of electronic food for the mind causes unrest and a lack of lasting comprehension. It's possible to moderate what has become a habit if you'll set aside a time and space without electronic communication. During that period and in that place, allow yourself to actually sit and communicate with a human. A computer won't exhibit facial responses, voice tone, and body language (not without Skype-type devices) or subtle transference of thought waves.

Those who think electronics can replace a human are deluding themselves. Or perhaps they're unaware of anything beyond the physical plane of existence. We human beings are privileged, standing upright and endowed with a powerful mind field capable of so much. Not even a state-of-the-art computer has such a life force. This life force that I am talking about is what gives you the power to feel good despite what is happening around you.

A developing trend to modify food production is also cause for concern because it, too, can short-circuit our relationship with nature. Our human body can't derive nourishment from synthetically made food and the increasingly popular genetically modified organisms (GMOs). Many clients have reported feeling ill after eating modified wheat, or genetically modified soy and corn. Like the computer, this "food" creates a new "language" unreadable by the body and our subtle mind field. It does not take a manipulated research study to realize that modified and polluted food is not vital, and food that is not vital cannot support a healthy and vital mind. Simply put, if something does not feel right to you, nix it as to not cause physical or mental indigestion. You don't need a study to tell you that it is so!

Remember that I stated food ultimately stores in our consciousness. Physical food blighted with chemicals, toxins, and DNA from non-natural sources is worthless to the body and negatively affects the mind. This concept is familiar to those with inner awareness, but others who ignore the seriousness of tampering with our food sources could witness the suffering bound to occur with increasing levels of anxiety, depression, and auto-immune disease.

I've heard others speak in defense of technology and its challenges to our human organism; they predict we'll evolve as in the past. My response is, "Evolve to what?" In the early decades of the 21st century, we're awash with technology developments that encourage quicker, more simple interaction, and facilitate still more multi-tasking than already has driven people to distraction. A decidedly lopsided picture is emerging, one that places value on material means to "do more things better," but ignores the spiritual and natural influences that must balance our lives.

IT'S A MATTER OF ENERGY

Energy is fundamental to all aspects of life. Each type of food, behavior, and lifestyle choice has an effect on us physically and mentally. To understand this, we must become familiar with the three subtle qualities, or *gunas*, that exist within the subtle realm manifesting throughout the universe in all realms of existence—from physical to spiritual. Because they are three constituent qualities of all nature and matter, these qualities constitute our thoughts and the foods we eat in different proportions, and so they directly affect our subtle energies that constitute how we feel.

To simplify, we can apply the concept of gunas as the "qualities" that are characteristic of all creation. Ultimately these qualities not only produce matter, but also keep changing it, depending on the quality of and strength of our consciousness. Here we speak about these three qualities in relation to our physical and psychological states.

Sattva, the first quality, is a state of harmony, balance, joy, and intelligence. Eating foods or engaging in habits with this quality produces serenity, an increased level of awareness, and a joyful and peaceful essence. Sattvic quality is the ultimate in nourishment for our organism and our mind field. The physical diet is vegetarian and the food is moist, fresh, and easily digestible.

Sattvic foods are fresh, juicy, light, nourishing, and sweet. They include well-prepared whole grains and legumes, fresh fruits, vegetables that grow above the ground, and, in some cases, dairy products from animals that are treated respectfully and grown in a chemical-free environment. These foods produce a calm and focused state of being. The digestive function produced from this energy source is good with regular and balanced intake and elimination.

A sattvic mind is one that is joyful and intelligent. It focuses on truthfulness and love. When someone is more sattvic in nature, she rarely experiences anger, pride, depression, and anxiety. She won't suffer distraction since her mind has clarity, calmness, and mental focus. With a sattvic mind, our awareness is good, attentiveness is strong, and creativity is quite high. It is a supreme place of contentment where the habits of one's life are on self-study, mantra and prayer, meditation, and self-reflection.

Tamas, the second quality, is a state of materiality and manifestation, as well as darkness, inertia, and inactivity. Tamas causes the "dull stupor" we experience after engaging in habits that make us sluggish and sleepy, and after eating meat and too many processed foods, sweets, and treats. The digestive function produced from this energy source is slow, with sluggish intake and elimination.

The end result is that we feel drained of energy and want to fall asleep. Tamasic foods include heavy meats, as well as foods that aren't fresh or have been chemically treated, processed, frozen, or refined. Genetically modified foods also would be tamasic, since they're lifeless to our organism. Canned and some frozen foods may provide macro- and micronutrients but lack the vibratory quality of freshly prepared foods. These foods produce lethargy, inertia, confusion, and fatigue.

More subtly, the tamasic lifestyle leads to ignorance and addictive and abusive behavior because this lifestyle dulls our awareness. You can see how it would be difficult to become engaged in what life has to offer if the tamasic quality were to take over. Tamasic lifestyle habits include excessive sleep and sexual activity, and activities of overindulgence.

A tamasic mind is lazy, immobile, and overindulges. Here we see that someone is not motivated to work or engage in healthy relationships since tamasic emotions revolve around dislikes, anger, pride, envy, and jealousy. A tamasic mind often experiences depression, anxiety, and distraction. It's difficult for someone feeding this type of energy to have mental focus and positive behavior since they're never content and their willpower and self-awareness is low. As you can imagine, creativity will be next to nonexistent because the awareness is clouded by inertia. When we change our diet and begin cultivating behaviors that support our heightened well-being, this energy can be transformed. Bringing movement into our lifestyle is needed, and that is the subject of the next quality.

Rajas, the third quality, is a state of action, change, and movement. The nature or quality of rajas is characterized by activity, movement, and attachment, as well as agitation and disturbance. This energy has the quality to take something that is inert and transform it into life. Rajasic foods are bitter, sour, salty, pungent, hot, and dry. They include fish, eggs, sweets, fried bread, raw onions, garlic, tea, and coffee. The lifestyle habits include those that fall into the category of "stimulation." Activities that arouse and artificially "rev up" the organism include excessive use of electronics, unbridled shopping, and traveling. The over-consumption of these foods and the lifestyle habits may create mental over-stimulation that leads to excesses such as greed, jealousy, anger, and self-indulgence.

We can suffer in other ways from this over-stimulation because it plays a role in hyperactivity and insomnia. Overuse of rajasic foods as well as living a rajasic lifestyle may leave you feeling full, whether in your stomach or your consciousness, but mostly you will feel unsatisfied. Rajasic lifestyle habits are those that are irregular and difficult to modify since they're variable.

A rajasic mind is active, restless, and agitated. One who is more rajasic will experience some sloth, on occasion, but not on a regular basis. In addition, since it's variable, the tendencies for depression, anxiety, and distraction fluctuate according to the day or time period. A rajasic mind does have some clarity but not without effort, and does experience calmness and mental focus most of the time. Irritability or impatience could be experienced since things might not move fast enough, but this energy does constitute variable willpower as well as self-awareness.

A lifestyle can have some or all three qualities. Rajasic can transform tamasic into more sattvic qualities. For example, we add spice to our meats so they're more digestible; we get up and go for a walk when we feel sluggish; we practice relaxation when we're agitated. Our entire organism is constantly trying to balance our energies into what is termed homeostasis, or balance. The path toward balance requires that we walk skillfully and carefully with total awareness in what feeds and nourishes our mind. With the knowledge of energy qualities, we can learn to navigate with a more calm and focused mind.

These aspects are interconnected. The more we're aware of the synergy of our existence with the world within us and the world outside, the better we're able to maintain homeostasis. Knowledge empowers us here. We know that our feelings don't exist in a sphere separate from our bodies, and food and lifestyle habits can affect how we feel. With this understood, we can learn to direct our energies so we feel good enough to walk through life joyfully.

Worthy of a mention: There is an important difference between directing and controlling. For now, we move on to understand the principles of what we call "mind," since our life's contentment depends on how well we use our mind.

PROMOTE A CALM AND FOCUSED MIND

So how can we start bringing the "sattvic" quality of nature into our lives? What follows is a practical list that may be useful in promoting a calm and focused mind.

Incorporate a more balanced habit into your life. Choose to begin making your environment more sattvic in nature.

1. Avoid watching any violence or harshness for entertainment.

2. Seek out the company of people who are positive.

3. Strive for composure in your words and actions and surround yourself with others who display equanimity and balance.

4. Consciously balance your day's meals—40% whole grains, 20% beans, 20% vegetables, 15% fruits and raw vegetables, and 5% dairy or meat.

5. When you receive a negative, discouraging, or disappointing message from your surroundings—a comment from a co-worker, a cross word from a friend, etc.—or when you find yourself thinking a negative thought about yourself (*"I'm a failure, lazy, inadequate..."*)—pause and say to yourself, *"Not today."* As you say, *"Not today,"* treat the negative words or interaction as a test of your centeredness. Will you take them in and dwell on them or acknowledge them and calmly wave them on? We defuse the toxicity of negative input when we learn anything we should from it and immediately move forward. I'll tell you what a good friend once told me: *"You have two ears; that's for letting junk go in one ear and out the other."*

THE THREE QUALITIES (GUNAS)

Our self-identity gives rise or expands into three qualities that pervade every aspect of the universe from the food we eat, to the thoughts we entertain, to our emotions and perceptions. It encompasses everything. These three qualities in the universe that pervade all are:

1. *sattva*—the quality of perfect balance, clarity, and purity, that which gives us our radiance;
2. *rajas*—the quality of movement and activity, that which gives us our passion and also connects the first quality with the last;
3. *tamas*—the quality of manifestation, which might be termed *inertia*.

All three qualities work together to where rajas, the quality of movement, expresses itself through the connection of sattva and tamas.

Review

TRUTH

What we feed our mind affects the quality of consciousness.

OBSTACLE

Allurement through our senses prevents our perfection.

EXIT STRATEGY

Be aware of what you feed your mind.

FACTS

- ❖ To change our mind, we must change what we feed it.

- ❖ All of nature is composed of three qualities.

- ❖ These qualities determine our body, mind, and consciousness.

- ❖ We can change how we feel by regulating our habits.

Path *of* Practice

"If you become capable of relaxing the body voluntarily, then you will be able to help your mind relax voluntarily. Mind is a more complex phenomenon. Once you have become confident that the body listens to you, you will have a new trust in yourself. Now even the mind can listen to you. It will take a little longer with the mind, but it happens."

—Osho

 JOURNAL ACTIVITY

Purpose:

Keep a diet record to become aware of your habits and how they influence your energy field.

Technique:

Have a nutritionally complete frozen meal one day and a freshly prepared version of the same the next.

1. Record how you feel after completing each meal, one hour later, two hours later, and on the following day. Noting your day-after responses is important, because that's when mood changes can really surface.

2. Continue for one week or until your new level of awareness changes how you select and prepare foods.

Core Practice

Systematic relaxation is a traditional yoga practice. It is a learned practice that can be applied after, as well as before, a meditation practice. It is a necessary element in establishing a calm and focused mind. You can attain relaxation if you train yourself. The pose— *Shavasana*— is perhaps one of the most important poses. It is called the "Corpse Pose" because, within a corpse, there is no effort. *Shavasana* positions our physical body to release the forces that keep us from experiencing psychological and emotional freedom, and releases "effort" itself. Thus, practiced daily, this has the capacity to rejuvenate the body, mind, and spirit.

Purpose:

To release the effects of stress by loosening the grip that binds the body experiencing physical and mental fatigue. To help absorb the nutrients by putting the body in a relaxed state.

Technique:

1. Lie down in *Shavasana* (Corpse Pose). Bring your mind to the vessel of the body. Calm the mind. Be still and intent. Here, in the supine position, go through the relaxation. Relax and soften the forehead, relax the eyebrows and eyes, relax the nostrils. Exhale and inhale a few times. (Pause)

2. Relax the cheeks, relax the jaw, relax the corners of the mouth,

relax the chin, soften and relax the neck muscles. Relax the shoulders, relax the shoulder joints, relax the upper arms, relax the elbows, relax the lower arms, relax the wrists, relax the hands, relax the fingers, relax the fingertips. Breathe as though the breath is flowing all the way through the fingertips. (Pause)

3. Relax the fingertips, relax the fingers, relax the hands, relax the wrists, relax the lower arms, relax the elbows, relax the upper arms, relax the shoulder joints, relax the shoulders. Relax the chest, relax the cardiac region. And gently exhale and inhale. (Pause)

4. Relax the stomach, relax the navel area, relax the lower abdomen, relax the thighs, relax the knees, relax the calf muscles, relax the ankles, relax the feet, relax the toes. Breathe as though the breath is flowing through the whole body, from top to toes, and toes to top. (Pause)

5. Relax the toes, relax the feet, relax the ankles, relax the calf muscles, relax the knees, relax the thighs, relax the lower abdomen, relax the navel area, relax the stomach, relax the cardiac region. (Pause)

6. Relax the chest, relax the shoulders, relax the neck muscles. Relax the chin, relax the jaw and the corners of the mouth, relax the cheeks, relax the nostrils, relax the eyes, relax the eyebrows, relax the forehead.

7. Relax and rest in the seat of your mind.

A Saying from the Sutras

Be friendly toward those who are not friendly

Have compassion for those less privileged

Be joyful for those who are happy
and "better than you"

Be indifferent toward the negative and positive.

"The mind is like the wind and the body is like the sand.
If you want to know which way the
wind is blowing, look at the sand."
—BONNIE BAINBRIDGE-COHEN, BODY-MIND CENTERING®

It's a Matter of Mind

We've learned that the gunas, or qualities, in nature are reflected throughout existence. We've reached the point where it is necessary for you to meet your mind. All along we've been talking about this mind being a powerful instrument and how it is prone to disturbance, distraction, and stupefaction. But what *is* this mind that we've talked about? We've learned that digestion is key to a healthy and vital body, and digestion of our thoughts, impressions, and experiences has the same effect as digested or undigested food on the body. Our problems must be digested; we can't think away the unthinkable.

We must create the skill to increase our mental digestive capacity. The key to this is to tame or train the mind. A trained mind knows that the ego is necessary to identify with our creator, but a weak ego that identifies with the objects of the world is the cause of our unhappiness and suffering. When we train our mind to stay on track, we experience more energy, focus, and fulfillment in life.

Our mind field has many appetites—likes and dislikes—that come from its sensory aspect. It's up to us, however, to decide what we want to feed it beyond physical food by way of impressions, thoughts, and experiences. We just need a good advisor. In this lesson, we'll learn that befriending our higher mind will allow us to recognize how ego-driven our motivations and decisions are.

RECOGNIZE THE FAMILIAR FACE OF FEAR

We might delude ourselves into believing we can think our problems away, but we really can't. No one wants to address personal mental hang-ups, but everyone has them. A mental hang-up is that which keeps us from being happy, focused, and calm. It takes the form of distractions, disturbances, and confusion.

As a society, we put a negative label on any "mental" problems, but are decidedly more sympathetic about physical issues. If the body and mind are one and the same, there's no difference. If we have a physical problem, we can dive deep into our unconscious to find a mental glitch that contributes to it. The logical course of action is to address any mental obstacles that prevent our happiness, working through them one at a time.

The aim of yoga science is to uproot mental blocks. Few would argue against a new paradigm for modern healthcare in which practitioners opt to "cure" problems through medication. There's such trepidation about examining and dealing with symptoms that often the goal is to quell the outward signs, although disharmony is just under the surface. Meditation is a useful tool to gain access to these conditions, but few are courageous enough to know who they are.

It's common to have mental hang-ups or entanglements; we can decide to face them and then get over them. Simply put, it's no big deal. Mental problems needn't be more debilitating than chronic colds, flu, cardiac disease, diabetes, fibromyalgia...you name it. People aren't always sympathetic toward others who experience depression or anxiety, thinking problems of the mind somehow don't qualify as illness. They could be dealing with arthritic pain or autoimmune disorders—chronic health issues—but they consider themselves separate from the plight of people with troubled minds. How ironic.

The mental illusion is never what it appears to be. What do I mean by this? Think of the weeds in a garden. Have you ever tried to pull up a weed, only to discover the root system a few feet away from the plant? This relates to any impediment that occurs in our mind-body complex. We think we have a low-back problem because our back is tired, but if we look for the cause of the problem, it's more than simply lifting something heavy. The weakness stems from instability in the muscular system—in the mind.

As we've learned, all our mental and physical issues are based in fear, the most basic primitive fountain that is the force behind all the rest. The fear of death is the most deeply embedded fear that all living organisms possess. People don't want to die, so they fight to spare their life even when the threat is only perceived. The cause of much illness is in some way linked to fear. That's the driving force. We acknowledge that organic physical issues exist, but here we consider how the thought, "What's going to happen to me?" plays a role in our convoluted thinking and behavior.

$$\smile\hspace{-0.3em}\backsim$$

PAY NO MIND TO THAT

Let's look at how fear drives distraction, disturbance, and stupe-faction. We have complexes, (mental) blocks, phobias, and neuro-ses renting space in our lower mind. Decide to face these; there's no need for embarrassment. We attempt to ignore them or believe we can hide them, but these problems can be seen behind our personality and our drama. I'll tell you that once we address our fears, we can begin to enjoy life and feel good.

What keeps the fear in place? The ego. It deludes us into faulty thinking. It blocks our heart repeatedly. In a healthy moment, our mind will take its counsel from the heart. That's when you have a moment of compassion and love. But if the ego is untrained and too strong, the mind will defer to it. That creates a big problem because the ego has a clear goal: to be seen, acknowledged, heard, and recognized. When we think we're inadequate but do things aimed at being "on top" and "the best," our ego is doing the counseling. The more unhappy we are, the "bigger" our ego.

When I use the word "ego" here, I refer to the part of our mind that *identifies* with who we *think* we are, not who we *actually* are—the Self. Our ego is the part of us that takes everything personally. *"I am happy." "I am sad." "I am a good teacher." "I am a bad teacher."*

This identification process is what creates our instability and false identification.

The world doesn't revolve around you or me; things just happen. Pause before answering this question: "Do you ever have a temper tantrum?" Don't be so certain if you answered, "no." How do you react to not getting what you want? Do you become disturbed? You might be surprised to learn that simple disturbance is a temper tantrum. How long do you maintain this reaction? Many of us behave in this way when we're not treated the way we expect, especially if we're not recognized for who we think we are.

I recall a perfect example with an incident during a professional training summit. The facilitator made a point of calling on students who hadn't volunteered; it was sort of a military approach creating an environment of stress. A friend, Lois, reacted by making mental judgments about how it wasn't right and how it shouldn't be allowed. She analyzed the instructor as being ego-driven and insensitive to the audience since she ignored the subtle energy that her aggressive behavior was eliciting among the students. When Lois was called upon, this relatively quiet and peaceful person reacted by reprimanding the teacher and saying she didn't want to feed into the behavior to enable this type of "teaching."

Lois' anger got in the way when she refused to answer the instructor's question, although she certainly knew the answer. I later asked Lois why this had happened, and she stalwartly proclaimed the teaching style was inappropriate for a classroom setting. "So what?" I asked. "Why were you so disturbed that you held onto your disapproval for so long?"

Once we think of our angry and irritated reactions as temper tantrums, we can start to work with ourselves. Since that incident, I've applied Lois' experience to myself. I began to view how many of my own reactions were based on my likes and dislikes—and how many of those likes and dislikes were rooted in fear.

Quite often, fear plays a role in developing our preferences. Our righteous thinking tells us, "This is the way things need to be," and we follow the pattern. It does so because, on one hand, our ego is always "better than" and on the other, we are simply afraid to let go of our beliefs in fear that our self-image and grand proclamations may crumble. We don't know our ego drives such thinking, because that's who we believe we are and we want to protect that at all costs.

We've learned here that our temper tantrums are ego-based. Mental imbalances can occur with our likes and dislikes. If we could identify our ego-based actions and reactions, we'd be happier because we wouldn't be pulled from our center of calm and focus. Keep in mind that transformation comes from practice, not only knowledge obtained from reading a book.

SEE THE NATURE OF MIND

Let's think of harnessing the energy or power of the mind as if training a horse. My experience with horses taught me ways to deal with the undirected energy of a young, never-ridden filly. The thoughtless method is termed "breaking a horse to saddle," as if the majestic steed were a pair of stiff leather shoes in need of a good stretch. I find this a poor choice of words because I wouldn't condone compromising a horse's spirit for the sake of riding it. In the complex training process, I earned the horse's trust by identifying her fears and pleasure points. Employing harsh methods would force the horse to accept a person's will, but the animal could emerge fearful and damaged psychologically.

Contrary to some long-held but misinformed theories, it's unnecessary to "show animals who's the boss" with force (the boss mentality is the ego here). Establish respect as the leader, or alpha, part of the relationship, and the horse will be receptive to training. The mind is not different: It needs to be led by the higher states of mind, not the ego. Follow your ego, and you will be led down a path of never-ending disillusion and misery.

To bring yourself to mental peace, become aware of what's causing the problem. Root up the real cause once you become aware of it. Re-inoculate your mind field with good food—thoughts, impressions, and relationships—to build a stronger and more resilient mind. Overwrite the old program. You will still "see" the memory, but you can disempower the interpretation and become indifferent to the image.

We begin by knowing and accepting who we are in simple self-acceptance. I use the acronym CALM for "Consciously Aware of Living in the Moment," because when we live in the moment, we become mindful and aware of our thoughts, speech, and actions. It becomes easier to find the root of our issues. Again, I must emphasize that we can't intellectualize this work. In other words, we can't rationalize and tell ourselves not to be anxious or depressed.

This reality must come from an inner dimension. It needs to occur after we become aware of our mental chatter that stems from fear—and don't react to it.

~

A DIGEST ON THE MIND'S METABOLISM

Prana, the subtle energy that sustains our life, can be sensory, neurological, or both. The mind, like the GI tract, has its own way to digest our thoughts, experiences, and impressions. We can determine a great deal about the state of our mind by observing our digestion. As we learned in the lesson on digestion, our bodies take in, assimilate, use, and store nutrients and eliminate the by-products from what we eat in a most amazing way. Our vitality depends on this. What we largely ignore is the fact that the state of our mental digestion, which is determined by how well we digest our thoughts, experiences, and impressions, creates the mind's level of vitality in a similar way.

The process of mental digestion starts when our senses take in impressions and data in what is called a *sensation*. The mind employs the senses to gain access to the outside world. Once that sensory data enters our mind, the process begins and a feeling is created. The condition of our mental metabolism determines how we will assimilate the information, which in turn influences whether or not our mind becomes balanced, stupefied, distracted, or disturbed.

When information is assimilated, we can choose to use it, eliminate what we don't use, or store it in memory to be used at a later time. One benefit of meditation, the subject of a later lesson, is that it helps a person efficiently eliminate the useless and fully employ the useful.

The four functions of mind (described below in detail) explain how we take in sensory impressions and data, assimilate it all under the influence of ego, use it, and decide to eliminate or store it. Nothing can be allowed to block or slow this process, or there will be consequences. As with physical digestion, mental digestion must work at its highest levels in order to maintain and operate the mind's daily functions. Physical constipation creates mental constipation, and vice versa.

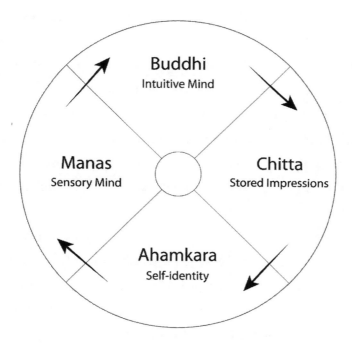

According to yoga science, the mind's functions can be described as four spokes on a wheel. Think of it as the wheel that transports us on the road of life. Let's examine this wheel more closely.

The **hub** represents the soul, the center of pure awareness, and the energy source that drives the wheel of life. Our center of pure awareness always remains still and unchanging since it's the true Self. This is the place of witnessing to which we seek access in our quest for psychological and emotional healing. We first must understand the four spokes of the wheel of life to get that access.

Although they work simultaneously, I'll describe the four functions of mind (wheel of life spokes) in a linear fashion. The sensory mind has five doors of perception (senses): smelling, tasting, seeing, touching, hearing. Some believe a sixth door is the mind itself. *Prana*, the energy or life force that permeates the entire universe, creates the sensation from the object that has been captured by the senses and carries it to the sensory mind.

The mind, or **manas,** constitutes the outer mind that interacts with the outside world to take in sensory impressions and generate feelings. It's the basis for our reasoning and allurement—that which pulls us away from doing what's best for us. The total mind is an instrument of feeling created by prana. We use this outer mind when we shop for clothing, sporting goods, or even a big-ticket car; our senses are likely to be awash with options, costs, and so on. This part of the mind isn't capable of making our decisions since it uses the senses only to gather information, but it enables our mind to experience the world and to fulfill its needs—to enjoy the sights, sounds, smells, tastes, and feel of the world around us.

It's best not to put this part of the mind in charge of decision-making. We leave that to the higher function of the mind, the intellect, or what is termed **buddhi**, the discriminatory aspect of mind. Regardless of what feelings are occurring, buddhi is the part of the mind that clearly sees things as they are. It's the ego that clouds the lenses of the buddhi. When indulged indiscriminately, the senses are capable of interfering with our ability to focus, since they draw the mind outward and away from the hub. It's this sensory aspect of our mind that tends to doubt and question. If allowed to be dominant, it can interfere with the ability to remain calm and focused.

We're better able to focus when we learn to seal our senses, rather than permitting them to drag us every which way, and choose what we want to be mindful of. Mindfulness is an exceptional tool for becoming aware of thoughts and not holding on to one or another. When we *bring our mindfulness into focus*, we choose among the potentially overwhelming inputs of our senses and learn to focus the lens of the mind. In this way, we gain access to higher levels of the mind.

Ahamkara is the third function of the mind, the one that gives us our sense of identity or "I." When it identifies with the sensory mind, ahamkara becomes part of the outer mind, but when it operates with the buddhi or discriminatory aspect, it is part of the inner mind. The highest form of ahamkara is knowing who we are from the core of our being. This is the universal mind in contrast with the individual mind.

Ahamkara has the capacity to identify with all the objects of the world. In this case, it becomes our individual ego that thinks and feels itself to be a separate entity, losing sight of the place of pure awareness or the "whole." When the ahamkara part of the mind isn't strong, we tend to think everything is "all about us," and that leads to making poor decisions.

When making a career choice, for example, you could set the criteria to reflect your skills and preferences, or to satisfy your desire for prestige. The latter would be a decision operating from the outer mind.

The perceived existence of "the enemy" is a common manifestation of ahamkara malfunction. No matter the form of the supposed antagonist, most people would agree to the existence of an enemy, somewhere, at some time. This adversary threatens our sense of identity, security, or status. The perception of someone or something as an enemy is in reality a choice, but this fact is impossible to see from the vantage point of the ego that fogs our lenses and distorts our vision. The ego works overtime to ensure we don't see that the adversary is constructed to maintain an insecure, inflated sense of individual importance.

When we make the choice not to create an adversary, we go beyond the ego and reach the place of the witness, the place of pure awareness, our Self, where our core energy is devoted to more important things, like supporting our vital mind. Both ahamkara and manas are the troublemakers; they have the potential to allure us away from what is right for us.

The discriminating mind, **buddhi**, is the part of the inner mind that judges and makes decisions and gives value to our feelings. Many books describe the buddhi as intellect, but this is often confused with what we view as intellectual. That's not the case here when we're discussing the four functions of mind. We could use the word "intellect" only if we understand it to be "the capacity to assign value to experience," as Rolf Solvik states in his book, *Moving Inward*.[30]

The higher aspect of mind also can be viewed as a doorway to our inner wisdom. It's the aspect we can bring into our awareness that has the capacity to give us the clarity and focus to decide and discriminate any thought, feeling, or object that comes into our mind field. Our training in meditation gives us the awareness to recognize the difference between the higher mind of buddhi and lower sensory aspect of manas. We ultimately want our sensory mind to take the back seat and let the higher functionality of buddhi to be the deciding factor. When this happens, our ability to focus and remain calm becomes strengthened. When we become aware of *who* is making the decisions and *who* is reading this book, we're operating from buddhi.

Awareness is the key to working with the functions of our mind field. And our awareness becomes strengthened when we learn the skill of being still, which ultimately comes from bringing our mindfulness into focus through meditation.

This aspect of our mind enables us to step back and evaluate. Acting out of buddhi, we're able to first recognize the appetites—products of the senses—then make decisions about the thoughts and appetites we want to acknowledge and those we want to let go. Our mind's inner fire (or metabolism) is heightened when we make decisions in this way, without the interference of our senses or the emotional memories of our ego.

The fourth function of mind is **chitta**, which collects images, creates the impressions, and stores them. Sometimes referred to as the "inner mind," it can be very useful in helping us move through life, but failing to coordinate chitta with the other three parts of mind can lead to difficulties.

Here's a simple example: You're invited to spend an afternoon cruising the harbor on a friend's boat. Your enthusiasm is tempered by a troubling childhood memory of someone falling into the water from a boat. Remembering danger or unconsciously bringing this impression forward, you choose not to board the boat. You're making a decision based not on what's best for you at the time, but as the result of a time that no longer exists except in your memory.

This part of mind feeds us in an unconscious way since we rarely have access to it (without proficient meditation). Such underlying memories are called *samskaras* in Sanskrit, for "a scar on the brain cell." Deep impressions travel with us through our neurological lineage. The image of whatever we've created is built by samskara; we interpret the image as good or bad and generate a thought about it. This colored thought that brings judgment with it is called an emotion.

I'm reminded of a client, Kate, who recently decided to adopt a dog while drawing on this kind of memory-based thinking. She missed the companionship of family dogs, the loyalty and love that these childhood pets provided. (Kate also wanted to exercise more and thought an energetic dog would prod her to take daily walks.)

So she set aside the facts: The dog in question was being given up by its current owner due to behavior problems; she worked long hours so the dog would be alone much of the time; and her newly remodeled home lacked a yard. You can see where this is going. After a week of chewed-up furniture, neighbors' complaints about barking, and walks with a dog who seemed only able to run, Kate was looking for someone to adopt *her* pet. Memories of a carefree youth, as well as her unmet emotional needs from the past, had clouded her contemporary decision-making. It would have been easier for Kate to make an appropriate decision if her memories didn't carry with them emotions that led to acting on desire.

MAINTAINING FOCUS IS SENSIBLE

Whereas ahamkara clouds the lens of the higher mind, meditation allows you to polish that lens to empower you to make discriminating decisions based solely on what's good for you at the time. This translates into confidence, fearlessness, and calm, clear focus over time.

Understanding these four functions of the mind helps us appreciate what goes on when we try to focus on something. For example, if we're bombarded by sensory input, it becomes too difficult to digest our experiences, not unlike eating too much food. This or that bit of sensory input may be more appealing or seem more important than the task at hand. Your genuine desire to finish up a project at your desk, for instance, can be sidetracked by a phone call from a friend or a story on the radio playing in the background. Focus can be a challenge, but the more energy or what we call "fire" that you cultivate, the more vital and clear your mind becomes so focus becomes attainable.

What type of appetite does your mind have? In the 2001 film, *A Beautiful Mind*, John Nash (played by Russell Crowe) delivers an eloquent final soliloquy. The Nobel laureate economist who battled schizophrenia says, "I have a problem with an unknown solution. However, all I have to do is apply my mind and I can solve the problem. Stress triggers my problems. If you feed your dreams or nightmares, whichever one [you feed] stays alive ... I choose not to acknowledge them ... I choose not to indulge in certain appetites ... Perhaps appetites are imagined."

As he fought his mental demons, Nash realized his life took on the color of whatever his mind focused on. He regularly saw people who were visible only to him. He acknowledged that the problem worsened under stress and that whatever images he chose to focus on stayed alive. He also discovered that the mind field has many appetites and that it loves to indulge in its own sensory aspect—the manas part of the mind.

Nash said he could choose to acknowledge the sensory mind or ignore it. This was his buddhi coming into play. He initially struggled to use the powerful faculties of his mind to *decide* what he would feed it, which was nothing more than developing the buddhi and determining a level of focus.

As we've learned, we must regulate the mind's appetite to develop clarity, calmness, and focus. This occurs by cultivating the awareness of how our mind works as well as what we feed our mind. A vital mind is one that has the ability to digest life's experiences to maintain the clarity and the ability to focus on *what* is necessary *when* it's necessary. It requires that we have an understanding of how energy is collected, contained, and circulated, which is the topic of our next lesson.

Review

TRUTH

Digesting thoughts & experiences affects the mind's vitality.

OBSTACLE

Your ego keeps fear in place.

EXIT STRATEGY

Listen to the heart, not the ego, to be free from fear.

FACTS

- ❖ You can't think your problems away.

- ❖ Look into the unconscious to find the mental glitch.

- ❖ Medicating the symptoms doesn't remove the cause.

- ❖ Transformation comes from changing your habits.

Path *of* Practice

"A man's mind may be likened to a garden, which may be intelligently cultivated or allowed to run wild; but whether cultivated or neglected, it must, and will, bring forth. If no useful seeds are put into it, then an abundance of useless weed seeds will fall therein, and will continue to produce their kind."

—JAMES ALLEN

 JOURNAL ACTIVITY

Purpose:

To become aware of the workings of the ego and higher Self so we can discover what allures us off our path.

Technique:

1. You can begin to assess the types of things that take you offtrack by observing the motivations behind your words or actions. This can have a profound impact and may surprise you, since sometimes we deny our true motivation.

2. You may also want to keep a record of whenever you use "I," "mine," or "me" so you can start to recognize how much of your interaction involves you, and how much time you remain in defense of yourself.

3. At the end of a day, you can record the things that you want to continue supporting and let go of those habits that prevent you from being honest with yourself.

Core Practice
61-POINT ADVANCED EXERCISE

These 61 points trace the outline of our subtle and physical bodies. It's derived from ancient texts and has been used for supporting a meditation practice. Why? Because it develops our power of concentration, not only in the physical sense, but also in the subtle sense. Concentration—focused awareness—can be affected by what is happening on our physical, energy, and mental level. So this practice allows us to tap into those levels and experience a deeper level of awareness.

Going through this exercise will train your mind to become one-pointed. It will allow your attention to be shifted inward and focused on the subtle inner levels of the mind/body connection and the vital energy that sustains our existence. That's why this exercise is so important and so powerful. It can be a beginner exercise, but it can also be an advanced exercise depending on how long you stay at each point.

The traditional name for the 61-point exercise is *Shavayatra* ("traveling through the corpse"). Its origin can be traced to *Vasishtha Samhita* and the Ayurvedic text, *Sushruta Samhita*. We want to travel through the body, not on a physical level, but on the subtle level, and this is the name's relevance. You will travel mentally throughout the body while reclining in the Corpse Posture.

Purpose:

A concentration practice that offers deep and complete release of tension of the physical body, the nervous system, as well as the deep pranic field—one's subtle energy—and the mind.

Technique:

1. Before beginning this exercise, you need to set a time when you won't be interrupted. You might want to get a shawl or blanket to cover yourself, because you'll go into deep relaxation while maintaining focus and the body will have a tendency to cool down.

2. To do this exercise focus on a blue or white point. The colors blue and white serve to calm the mind, while others will have a different effect. For example, red will stimulate the mind. If you choose not to focus on color, then use numbers as you travel throughout the body.

3. Begin by preparing a space where you can lie down without interruption. Lie on a mat or carpeted floor. Place a small pillow under the head for support. Place the feet about 8-12 inches apart and the arms and hands slightly away from the body, palms facing up.

4. Establish an even and steady breath. As you move to each point keep this rhythm and set the intention to expand and soften the point.

5. To derive added benefit, move to each point with an exhalation, maintaining the calm and balanced rhythm of inhalation and exhalation that you have established.

6. Start with a cleansing breath for one or two minutes. Inhale through the toes to the top of the head, then exhale down from your head through your toes. Repeat this five times, imagining filling your body with positive vibration on an inhalation, and on an exhalation, letting go of any residual tension.

7. Bring your attention to space just above the point between the two eyebrows and see a light or think the number "1". Continue focusing on either the light or the corresponding numbers. See sequence below. Choose two seconds to start. You can expand if your mind does not wander. The key is to spend the same amount of time at each point.

THE SEQUENCE IS AS FOLLOWS:

1) point above the space between the eyes; 2) hollow of the throat; 3) right shoulder joint; 4) right elbow joint; 5) middle of the right wrist; 6) tip of the right thumb; 7) tip of the index finger; 8) tip of the middle finger; 9) tip of the fourth finger; 10) tip of the small finger; 11) right wrist joint; 12) right elbow joint; 13) right shoulder joint; 14) hollow of the throat; 15) left shoulder joint; 16) left elbow joint; 17) middle of the left wrist; 18) tip of the left thumb; 19) tip of the index finger; 20) tip of the middle finger; 21) tip of the fourth finger; 22) tip of the small finger; 23) left wrist joint; 24) left elbow joint; 25) left shoulder joint; 26) hollow of the throat;

27) heart center; 28) center of right side of the chest; 29) heart center; 30) center of the left side of the chest; 31) heart center; 32) solar plexus, just above the navel; 33) center of pelvis, two inches below the navel; 34) right hip joint; 35) right knee joint; 36) right ankle joint; 37) tip of right big toe; 38) tip of the second toe; 39) tip of the third toe; 40) tip of the fourth toe; 41) tip of the small toe; 42) right ankle joint; 43) right knee joint; 44) right hip joint; 45) center of pelvis, two inches below the navel; 46) left hip joint; 47) left knee joint; 48) left ankle joint; 49) tip of left big toe; 50) tip of the second toe; 51) tip of the third toe; 52) tip of the fourth toe; 53) tip of the small toe; 54) left ankle joint; 55) left knee joint; 56) left hip joint; 57) center of pelvis, two inches below the navel; 58) solar plexus, just above the navel; 59) heart center; 60) hollow of throat; 61) center just above the space between the eyebrows.

8. Continue breathing steadily. Next, inhale from the toes to the top of the head and exhale from the top of the head to the toes. (Pause.) Repeat several times and be aware of your body. Without breaking your rhythm, breathe as though the entire body is breathing through all the points. Allow yourself to transition gradually by bringing the hands in front of the eyes, opening them gently. Wiggle the toes and fingers. (Pause.) When ready, roll onto your left side, and get up.

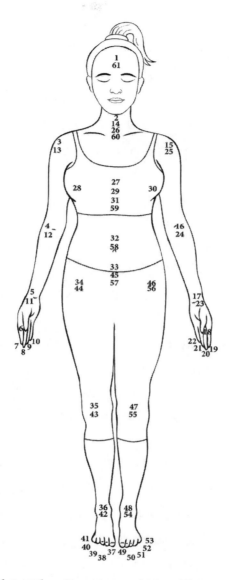

This completes the 61-point exercise. This exercise is fundamental to any meditation practice. It is ancient and has always
been used to perfect the concentration of the mind so practitioners can go beyond the mind to obtain mastery over the meditation

process. If you find yourself getting bored or distracted, pay attention to see at what point in the body this occurs. It may relate to what's going on psychologically with you. Just as an example, suppose you have real issues with being assertive. Perhaps when you get to the navel center, you may be distracted or bored. Boredom means you just aren't paying attention. When you pay attention, you don't get bored.

Don't be discouraged with this exercise; it's an advanced exercise. Learn to play with it. Move through the points faster if you find yourself getting distracted. But start training the mind. It's better to do a few correctly than to not do it at all.

Don't start with 20 seconds at each point. If you haven't done something like this before, you will surely want to fall asleep. So you need to pay attention to your own rhythm and your own thoughts. When do you get distracted or bored? When do you just want to get up? Pay attention to where that happens in your body. It might be a clue to other things that could be happening in your body.

This exercise is very potent in developing awareness. It can serve as a useful tool when you're getting to know yourself and how you operate. It can also help you realize or become aware of the energy flow within your body. Do you notice that you've actually done a scanning on your body—not only your physical body but also your subtle body? By mastering scanning, you learn to assess what's going on.

So you ask, "How necessary is this?" It can be quite necessary, because when you become in tune with what's going on within yourself, you can correct it and make changes. When you bring your awareness to each of those points, your focus increases and your awareness turns inward, allowing you to go to the deeper levels within yourself. Awareness at the deeper levels allows you to direct the energy to wherever you want it to go. That's what the practice is all about.

"When the mind is calm and tranquil, sushumna, the central channel, is awakened. The joy derived from the mind traveling through the sushumna channel is unique; it cannot be compared with any sensory pleasure. Because of that inner joy, the mind loses its taste for worldly pleasures. Sushumna application is the most important factor in spiritual practice."

—**Swami Rama**

LESSON 10

It's a Matter of Energy Channels

We now move from our head to our heart. Getting access to the heart, we learn to read the language of the living mind—living, because this is where we gain access to what keeps us flowing freely to live life's purpose. We've learned that our energy needs to be collected, contained, and circulated; now it's time to delve more deeply into what this means and how it works.

In this lesson, we conclude with a practice that gives us access to our own internal GPS, our energy pathways. We know that vitality, our inner fire, is easily extinguished by negativity and self-neglect and is very difficult to rekindle. So it makes sense to pay attention to our vitality with the devotion of a mother tending to her child.

This lesson teaches us how to collect, contain, and circulate vital energy to maintain our physical health and mental balance.

GO WITH THE VITAL FLOW

If we look at our energy channel as a river system with an origin, pathway, and outlet, we come to understand and know that our body and mind operate with the same principles found in nature. If we understand how our energy flows in addition to where it starts and ends, we gain access to what drives our own healing force. When the energy flow is impeded or exceeded—in other words, not balanced—we experience anxiety or depression, or both interchangeably. This is how both anxiety and depression become a whole-body problem and not just a mental problem.

For example, the manifestation of our mind begins in our brain, heart, and *chakras*. The pathway moves and influences the layers of our being, called *koshas*, where there are five, starting from the most subtle—our inner light—to the grossest—our physical body. The opening of these pathways is found in the synapses of the brain, *marma* (acupuncture points) and our sensory organs. We can use these openings as a way to manipulate even the subtlest of energy, which explains why acupuncture, or marma therapy, works to heal our organism. Understanding this, we can develop practices to get access to our own energy channels in order to unblock, stimulate, and ultimately heal ourselves.

The word *nadi* literally means "flow or current," analogous to a river system. While not part of the physical body, nadis serve as energy pathways; the ancient texts say we have an astonishing

72,000 of them. Chakras are where many of the energy currents cross to create a hub. Both the nadis and chakras are part of our subtle or psychic body. A marma point is where a few of these currents cross over each other, so more energy is present at this place of intersection.

According to yoga science, wherever prominent energy currents meet or cross over in our bodies, there's a chakra (a Sanskrit word meaning "wheel"). These inner whirlpools govern our physical, emotional, mental, and spiritual well-being. They serve as formatting templates for the mind. Yoga science, Taoism, and other Eastern philosophical systems regard chakras as centers of energy: the life force or *shakti*. In essence, these are simply ways of talking about our subtle energy vitality.

From a Western scientific perspective, the chakras are neurophysiological axes. They're associated with nerve plexuses that, although not physical in nature, theoretically exist in the spinal column as well as outside. The solar plexus, for example, is commonly assumed to lie in the abdominal region. Physicians will recognize that when a patient refers to it; a martial artist will understand it as the "hara"; but the solar plexus can't be located by an x-ray or MRI (magnetic resonance imaging). So the notion of "theoretical plexuses" is already enshrined in the Western view of the body.

Each chakra is also associated with certain endocrine glands and internal organs and has a psychological significance that we'll discuss shortly. The first chakra *(mooladhara)*, associated with the earth element and stability, is located at the base of the spine. It encompasses the perineum, rectum, and prostate gland.

The second (*swadhisthana*), associated with the water element and the subconscious mind and sleep, is located at the perineum, between the anus and genital organ in a male, and at the posterior side of the cervix midway between the vagina and uterus in the female. It's related to the lumbar plexus—the female and male reproductive and urinary systems.

The third (*manipura*) is associated with the element fire and the digestive organs. It is located at the solar plexus, where it governs the adrenals and pancreas. The third chakra is our metabolic center, physically as well as emotionally and psychologically.

The fourth (*anahata*) is the heart chakra, associated with the air element, which is the seat of consciousness. This place where the living mind dwells is located at the heart level. All energy flows through this chakra. It's associated with the cardiac plexus, thymus gland, and pericardium. We can gain access to this center by working with the third and sixth chakra.

The fifth chakra (*vishuddhi*), associated with the ether element, is located at and related to the thyroid gland, at the level of the throat. It also is connected to the vagus nerve and cervical ganglion. This energy center connects our heart to our head.

The sixth chakra (*ajna*) is known as the command center, the seat of the mind. It has no element of association, but correlates with the pineal gland. It's the point of confluence where the three main nadis or forces—*ida, pingala, and sushumna*—merge into one stream of energy that move up to the seventh chakra.

The seventh chakra (*sahasrara*) is located at the crown of the head and is associated with supreme consciousness beyond the physical dimensions. Some systems posit an eighth and ninth chakra, as well.

Yoga science teaches us to work through the lower three chakras, moving from our instinctual urges to reach the space of consciousness known as the heart chakra. Working with the third chakra *manipura*, or *hara* in Japanese, we ignite our fire and improve our digestion, immunity, and confidence level. It helps to move and lift energy through the first two. Working with the sixth chakra, or *ajna*, we gain command over the pranic energy flow, which helps us gain access to our heart. It is the foundation for any work in self-development and transformation.

There are many excellent books on the profound action and implications of the chakra system. When we're in complete balance, vitality flows through all seven chakras. The three that we have focused on here are the third, sixth, and fourth. The third governs our vital energy, is the most accessible, and lifts our energy through the first two chakras; the sixth is our command center for pranic flow and, when reached, gives us the ability to focus all our energy fields; the fourth is the home of the living mind where our feelings dwell. When we move and operate from our heart, we live with compassion, love, and luminous joy.

HAPPINESS IS A HARMONIOUS HARA, HEAD, AND HEART

The Sanskrit word for "mind" is *chitta*, which also means heart. The same word is used for heart and mind in several other Asian languages. Our feeling good depends on the balance between the hara, head, and heart. Let's see why.

The first (or lower) three chakras are the basis for our animal instincts: matters of survival, procreation, and self-preservation. Ideally, we work with the third chakra, *manipura* or hara to gain access to metabolic and radiant energy, then take that newly found energy and bring it into focus at the sixth chakra, *ajna*. Here it is intensified to light the path for us to reach the space of consciousness, the heart chakra, *anahata*, where ultimate joy resides.

In the first five chakras, the elements of earth, water, fire, air, and ether blend with the senses of smell, taste, sight, touch, and sound. All are connected to the internal organs through the autonomic nervous system and the nadis (subtle energy channels). Allowing the dormant energy that resides at the base of the chakra system to rise through the chakras sounds like a simple matter, but actually doing it takes a lot of practice. We encounter physical and psychological roadblocks at every level, and we can become stuck in any one of them. We work with the three we have chosen to create a systematic approach.

While the lower chakras allow us to enjoy the sensuous pleasures of our world, getting stuck there creates problems and keeps us from experiencing a full spiritual life. Moving through them by working with the "hara" helps us remove fear and self-doubt as we gain confidence and determination to serve in the world. The hara, or *manipura,* chakra is the most accessible and hence, it is easiest to start our journey here.

In our competitive culture, for example, many of us are drawn off course by the illusion of control and dominance. Fear and lack of inner security generates aggression, anxiety, jealousy, and anger. When we don't get what we want, we can become depressed or have a temper tantrum. These are sure signs that we're stuck in the third energy center, which is connected with the element of fire. Our fiery, tempestuous personality may manifest in skin irritations, ulcers, overheating, hypoglycemia, digestive problems, insomnia, anxiety, or even a sluggish liver. Keep in mind that fire is the only element that must be tended to. Therefore, our practices are designed to tend to this center.

We can take that newly accessed energy and bring it to the eyebrow center, or the sixth chakra. At this point, we can concentrate and refine the fire so this area becomes illuminated. Fire in this context becomes the light that gives us clarity and vision so we don't become bogged down with obstacles. Concentration practices enable us to access this center. Once established, we have the makings to remove the obstacles that bind the heart and gain entry.

The heart is a very special place and must be protected from our likes and dislikes, pleasure and pain, and impressions that keep us feeling dejected, anxious, and fearful. Once we reach the abode of the heart—the fourth chakra—we begin to shine with the joy and luminosity that is our birthright.

At this level, we're less tied to our physical world. We can begin to integrate aspects of higher emotions and compassion as our consciousness begins to evolve. This is where we no longer have animosity, jealousy, anger, and resentment. We have compassion for others' suffering and understand our purpose in life. We literally *step into the light* and come to recognize that our purpose in life is to serve others.

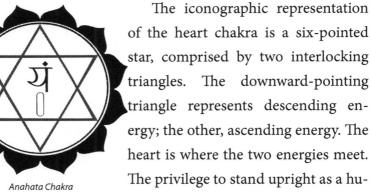

Anahata Chakra

The iconographic representation of the heart chakra is a six-pointed star, comprised by two interlocking triangles. The downward-pointing triangle represents descending energy; the other, ascending energy. The heart is where the two energies meet. The privilege to stand upright as a human being gives us access to the innate powers that enable us to overcome obstacles that prevent us from experiencing love, joy, and compassion.

The seventh chakra is another meeting place, this time, of the spiritual and the sensual. When the two come together, we experience full self-awareness and realization. We're on the threshold of what the ancient adepts with knowledge refer to as "enlightenment."

These descriptions illustrate how the energy of the chakras serves as doorways to the realm of our existence. They are associated with the spinal column but are not confined in the body. They extend beyond the boundaries of the physical body.

We don't operate in any one chakra at a time. Our body-mind-spirit is a holistic continuum in which every event affects all the processes at play throughout. So whatever issues are being processed at the various levels, they're dealt with simultaneously, not sequentially. One center may predominate, but all function continuously, influencing their own areas as well as each other's areas.

To understand how energy moves through the chakras, try thinking of our energy system as a spiraled staircase. As we've noted, our energy travels from the first or root chakra at the base of the spine—ground floor—to the penthouse abode of the highest, the crown chakra. Moving up this imaginary staircase, our life energy passes the five other floors. Each of these floors houses different offices engaged in different types of activity. Although energy is designed to move freely up the staircase, it can become trapped in any one of these offices. When that happens, it can't fully or effectively reach the higher floors.

For example, you're preoccupied with your livelihood. It's a common problem to experience concerns (even fear) about how one is going to survive financially. This preoccupation keeps you stalled at the first chakra. Consequently, you experience issues manifesting with your bowels, lower back, and anything else connected with the notion of physical or psychological support (pelvis, legs, ankles, etc.). If you aren't aware that these problems originate in energy stagnating on your "ground floor," you'll waste a lot of time and energy trying to treat or escape the symptoms. These attempts can become ingrained as habitual patterns, which eventually plant their roots deep in your psyche. And hence, a condition or disease is born.

Disease states can be recognized and understood when you have access to the energy patterns of all the chakras. The body serves as an excellent vehicle for us to learn how to untie the subtle energy knots that bind us, since the body is a reflection of these energy fields.

⌒

LOOK INSIDE FOR DIRECTION

Out of a large number of nadis, the three most important are *ida, pingala,* and *sushumna,* which serve as our internal GPS. Our car's satellite-guided navigation system and these three nadis, accessible through our nasal region, operate in much the same way. When ida, pingala, and sushumna are flowing fully, we can navigate harmoniously through life. Disease states occur when this flow is interrupted or blocked.

Ida (pronounced like the woman's name) is the channel that originates from the left side of the first chakra—the *mooladhara*—and spirals up the spinal column as it passes through each chakra, forming a crossing-over pattern that terminates at the left side of the sixth chakra, or ajna chakra. The pingala nadi is a channel that originates from the right side of the mooladhara chakra and mirrors the ida nadi, terminating at the right side of the ajna chakra.

These two forces are the opposite forces operating within us. They can be monitored by watching the flow of breath through our nostrils. For example, when ida is dominant, breath flows through our left nostril and we have more activity with those organs connected to the parasympathetic nervous system. When breath is more dominant through the pingala nadi, we have more activity in the organs of the sympathetic nervous system. This translates into different physical and mental activities.

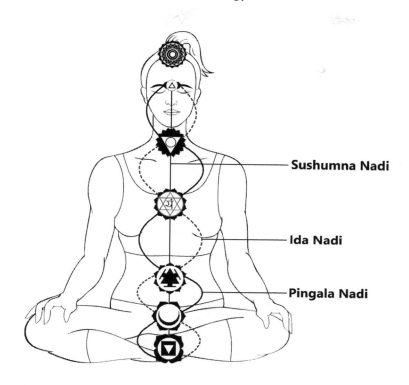

Sushumna Nadi

Ida Nadi

Pingala Nadi

The right nostril, or *pingala*, is represented by the sun and other images of heat. It is associated with the left brain and sympathetic nervous system responses. Digestion is more effective when your right nostril is flowing, so after eating a big meal, if you feel lethargic and can't digest, try activating your right nostril. Open it up, and digestive enzymes will begin to flow.

When clients tell me they eat by the clock, not in response to hunger, I ask them to start paying closer attention: When the right nostril has more air flowing through it, the digestive system is ready to take food. Simply focusing on the right nostril will help you to go for a bike ride or vigorous walk, because your muscle strength and physical energy are maximized. When the right nostril is active, your analytical thinking is also engaged. You are apt to have more REM (rapid eye movement) sleep then, as well.

Then we have *ida*, which is the left nostril. Ida is associated with the moon; it's cool and moist, producing a relaxing and receptive state of mind, and it's identified with the parasympathetic nervous system. Breathing on the left gives us a greater tendency toward intuition. We'll be more likely to drink than eat when our left nostril is flowing more.

Chances are that if we find ourselves feeling lethargic, our left nostril has been dominant for longer than its natural 90-minute or two-hour cycle. Left-nostril breathing doesn't support logical or analytical thought, so consider this if you're having trouble reasoning your way through a problem.

Sushumna is the central channel and is located in the center of the spinal column. It originates at the first chakra and terminates in the *sahasrara chakra* at the crown of the head. The soft spot on the head of newborn babies is perhaps the most important nadi in the entire network.

The sushumna channel is operating when both nostrils are flowing evenly, which occurs at the point of shift after a 90-minute to 2-hour session of nasal dominance. For a few seconds, when that shift takes place, the central channel is open. At that time we experience our greatest integration of consciousness. Both sides of the brain are equal and our mind disengages from worldly activities, turning inward. That time span, that window of opportunity, is so short that we hardly notice it.

WE CAN CHANGE CHANNELS ON DEMAND

During meditation, it's necessary to have both nostrils flowing evenly with the central, or shushumna, channel open to achieve the most benefit from the practice. Many practitioners adjust their lifestyle habits—including sleep, sex, and food—to accommodate this physiological process.

One way to start is by learning to become aware of the flow of breath through your nostrils. Is your left more active than your right, or is your right more active than your left? There are certain physiological and psychological manifestations and activities associated with right and left nostrils. Right-nostril dominance is linked to the left brain, and thus, physical activity; increased body heat; hunger; eating and digesting food; and short-term, intense effort. In contrast, left-nostril dominance is tied to the right brain, and thus, quiet receptive activity, body coolness, thirst, drinking liquids, and long-term, sustained effort.

The first way of changing your nostril dominance is to lie on the opposite side of the nostril you want to open. If you need your right nostril to be open, lie on your left side; if you need your left to be open, lie on your right side. The length of time it takes to open a nostril depends on where you are in each 90-minute to 2-hour cycle. If you just started a new cycle and you want to switch, it might take you a little longer than if you were at the end of the cycle.

But suppose you can't lie on the floor and you need a change. For instance, you feel a headache coming on when you're about to make a presentation at a conference. Common sense prevents you from lying on the floor in the middle of the meeting, but you can sit with your arm over a chair. Your right arm over the chair will open the left nostril; the left arm over the chair will open the right nostril. The key is to apply pressure under the armpit where nerve receptors will help.

Becoming aware of one's nostril dominance is dramatically empowering. Both students and clients are thrilled by the ways they can apply this knowledge to their daily lives. For example, I ask participants in my workshops to note which nostril is dominant when they wake in the morning. They unanimously report that, if they feel tired and reluctant to rise, the left is more active. Those ready to rise and shine find the right is more active. Anyone who has trouble getting going in the morning can use this tool to gently alter that situation.

This awareness can help us when we're dealing with symptoms relating to depression or anxiety. Another example: Many times, when clients arrive complaining of depression, I explain that they need to "activate" themselves. These people usually find that the left nostril is dominant most of the time and they don't experience the standard 90-minute to 2-hour shift pattern. Getting up and becoming active earlier in the day, as well as incorporating special pranayama and yoga practices to activate the right nostril (and, thus, the left hemisphere of the brain) will help these people because this causes the right nostril to become dominant.

Activating either the right or left nostril is not like taking a pill that can be prescribed. One person may have a fever and a blocked right nostril, while another has a fever with a blocked left nostril. The etiology of each person's condition differs. So I prefer to work with *awareness* of dominance, adapting our activities to correspond whenever possible.

But when we do want to make a change, consider massaging or otherwise stimulating the nostril you want to open, either with a finger, tissue, or nasal wash. You can also change nostril dominance by concentrating on breathing warm air into the nostril you want to open, while at the same time using your mind and imagining that the nostril is being opened. (You need a concentrated mind to do this.)

If your right nostril is closed, you can also focus on creating active thoughts, and, if possible, get your body up and moving. If your left is closed, imagine coolness or that you're lying in water; or put on some soothing music. Experiment with these techniques and see what works best for you.

When we understand how our subtle channels operate and how they're integrated with the mind, mystery dissipates and we can become a writer of our life. We realize that we're not a passive recipient at the mercy of events "out there" or of our changing moods. We observe our Self, tuning in to shifts in energy. We pay attention to our breath; we become aware of ways we can modulate energy and influence our mental and physical states through breath adjustments.

There's a clear scientific foundation for nostril dominance called *swara yoga*, and knowing about it makes it easier to regulate our activities—to rest when it's time to rest and play when it's time to play—never forcing an activity that isn't appropriate given our energy at that time.

When students discover they can change the way they breathe and consequently influence how they think and feel, they join the ranks of people not just inhabiting their bodies, but also acting as the architects and inspirations of their lives. Learning how our emotional health can be brought into alignment is the topic of our next lesson.

"Feelings come and go like clouds
in a windy sky.
Conscious breathing
is my anchor."
—Thich Nhat Hanh

Review

TRUTH
Depression & anxiety are a whole-body problem.

OBSTACLES
Improper breathing & thinking disrupts our vital energy flow.

EXIT STRATEGY
Cleansing & nourishing our energy channels.

FACTS
- ❖ Energy must be collected & circulated to remain vital.

- ❖ Breath, thought, and feelings affect our energy pathways.

- ❖ A balanced nervous system helps contain & circulate energy.

- ❖ Open energy channels give us the vitality to feel good.

Path *of* Practice

"As a fire blazes brightly when the covering of ash over it is scattered by the wind, the divine fire within the body shines in all its majesty when the ashes of desire are scattered by the practice of pranayama."

—B.K.S. IYENGAR

 JOURNAL ACTIVITY

Purpose:

To become aware of the subtle energy pathways that nourish the brain and balance the mind.

Technique:

1. Take note of which nostril is dominant when you get up in the morning. You can assess which nostril is dominant by closing off one and then the other to see which one has more air flowing through it. (If you're more sensitive, you may be able to do this without using your hand.)

2. Notice how you feel: awake or tired, hungry or not.

3. By evaluating your body in this way and using it as a feedback mechanism, you'll learn to open up the channels and bring back flow to the place that might have been neglected.

Core Practice

Alternate Nostril Breathing – *Nadi Shodhanam*
(The queen of all practices.)

This is a core foundation practice. To alternate the flow of air between the right and left nostrils means balancing and purifying the energy channels associated with the right and left nostrils and right and left hemispheres of the brain. Once mastered, you have access to your internal GPS (global positioning system) that allows your energy to be collected, contained, and circulated.

With this exercise, you breathe through only one nostril at a time. The logic behind this exercise is that normal breathing does alternate from one nostril to the other at various times during the day. In a healthy person, the breath will alternate between nostrils about every 90 minutes to 2 hours. Because most of us are not in optimal health, this time period varies considerably between people and further reduces our vitality.

According to the ancient healing traditions, when the breath continues to flow in one nostril for more than 2 hours, as it does with most of us, it will have an adverse effect on our health. If the right nostril is involved, the result is mental and nervous disturbance. If the left nostril is involved, the result is chronic fatigue and reduced brain function. The longer the flow of breath in one nostril, the more serious the illness will be.

Ancient healing traditions use this exercise to cleanse and rejuvenate the vital channels of energy, thus the name *Nadi Shodhanam* (purification of nadis or channels).

Purpose:

To clear energy channels, calm the nervous system, promote emotional stability, and support a meditation practice by linking the mind with the breath.

Technique:

1. Raise the right hand and bring the first two fingers and rest them between the eyebrows or fold them toward the palm..

2. Bring the thumb to the right side of the nose and the ring finger to the left side. We'll start by taking an exhalation and an inhalation through the left nostril three times, followed by taking an exhalation and inhalation through the right nostril three times. For the practice here, each breath will be synchronized to a count of three. With continued practice this count will increase.

3. Round 1—Begin and inhale smoothly and evenly through both nostrils for a count that is natural without feeling strained

or breathless. Gently, close off the right nostril with the thumb, exhale through the left nostril, and inhale through the left nostril with little to no pause. Try to feel the breath extending from the navel region to the eyebrow center on the inhalation and on the exhalation, back down. Repeat this three times, exhaling through the left and then inhaling through the left.

4. On the third inhale, switch and close off the left nostril with the ring finger. Exhale through the right nostril and inhale through the right nostril again with little to no pause. Do this three times on this side.

5. Now remove the hand and breathe through both nostrils for three complete breaths, exhaling and inhaling through both nostrils smoothly and evenly.

Summary:

This completes one round. Start by doing three rounds, adding one per week until you're doing seven cycles.

Note: *You can use the left hand to do this practice with the thumb positioned on the left nostril and the ring finger positioned on the right nostril.*

"There is no fire like passion,
there is no shark like hatred,
there is no snare like folly,
there is no torrent like greed."

—BUDDHA

It's a Matter of Emotion

We continue our journey to the Self by taking a look at our emotional body. Springing from the four primitive urges—food, sleep, sex, and self-preservation—emotions are powerful. The most transformative is love, followed in strength by joy and contentment. Addressing our emotional life enables us to begin to harness our energy and use it to sustain and live our life's purpose. Our life is filled with experiences; every event leaves a trace in our mind field. With our feelings and thoughts, we color these memories as positive or negative and create emotions.

The key to dealing with emotions is to recognize their source, some of them deeply buried in our subconscious. The purpose of this lesson is to teach us how to get access to this store of images and memories so we can start to heal.

FEELINGS DON'T TOUCH ON REALITY

The importance of emotions—as they relate to our capacity to sustain energy and focus—makes it imperative that the subject be examined in this book. Emotions are one of the major pillars of our foundation, and we need to work with them on a daily basis by understanding their source in order to learn how to get off the emotional roller coaster that sends us on fluctuating ups and downs throughout the day.

We first heal our emotions by understanding their nature and how they arise, then work with images and feelings. In comparison, we would heal our mental field by working with our thought constructs and heal spiritually through pure awareness. All levels can be trained when we bring mindfulness into focus.

The root of the word emotion is "motion." Nothing can cause turmoil and movement like our emotions, and the battle to remain calm is constant. How does it happen? We're complex organisms with past memories stored throughout our lifetimes. The word *samskara* is our storehouse of memories—little scars sustained from emotionally charged situations that are retained as memories. Remember that those memories aren't local; they're within the universal mind field. So when we work with emotions, it's critical to recognize that they're a reaction to our past memories triggered by a present challenge.

Stored as images in our subconsciousness, these memories automatically arise in our consciousness when we deal with a situation. Emotions flower from desire. If our desire is fulfilled, we experience positive emotions; if our desire isn't fulfilled, we experience negative emotions. When our senses perceive an object—whether through through hearing, touching, seeing, tasting or smelling—this perception is influenced by what memories (images) are stored in our mind. We experience this process as a feeling. We don't even realize where our feelings are coming from because we aren't aware of certain past memories that we keep as images. This feeling creates a thought, which is our way of describing the experience to ourselves. The thought can be pure, neutral or emotionally colored, depending on how refined and polished our ego is.

Ego is our image maker. It likes to be in charge and identifies with things that aren't really who we are; in essence, it's what deludes us into forming our preferences and dislikes. If anyone is to blame it is the ego for it initiating the problems. It's the ego that creates the image through its identification, and, depending on what image surfaces from our memory, a thought and/or emotion is created.

See how the ego's role is illustrated by this example. Introduce two people, Carol and Michael, to the same dog. Carol is immediately frightened and backs away. Michael stoops down to stroke the dog without fear. What is the reason for such different reactions? Perhaps Carol wasn't raised with a dog or as a child was bitten by one so she identifies with and holds onto the pain associated with her experience; Michael could have fond memories of a family pet. Each person perceives the dog as something else: Carol sees it as danger that could cause physical pain. Michael perceives the dog as a source of pleasure associated with his childhood. Carol generates a reaction from the feeling, which then creates the thought, "*I have to get back. This dog might bite me,* while Michael thinks, *I want to pet this dog. It reminds me of the one we had when I was young.*" Carol sees the dog's teeth as menacing. Michael entices the dog to lick his hand.

Thoughts are endless, and when acted upon, create an emotion. In essence, an emotion sets our thoughts into action. I'm simplifying the linear nature for the sake of example, but it illustrates the complexity of our mind field and its interaction with the outside world through our senses.

PUT MEMORY INTO PERSPECTIVE

The sutras of yoga science say, "Yoga is the cessation of chitta" (here meaning *memory*)[31] Notice the act of cessation—in contrast to erasing—of memory. Cessation requires that we observe (remain calm) and not put into action the thoughts that arise from the images created by ego. This is the ultimate in remaining calm and not allowing thoughts to dictate how we feel and act. Remember, emotions aren't thoughts. Thoughts are constructs of the mind. Emotions are generated as a result of whether we choose to identify with those thoughts. When we have associations with our perceptions, we create emotion

Perception is pure light—
a reflection of the soul—
but when influenced by ego, it becomes clouded.

If our image maker or ego is polished, there are no dislikes and likes; we just see everything as is, without judgment. We're the observer not involved in the mental dialogue of the sensory mind.

We work with our emotions by first being aware of our perceptions and the feelings that are housed in the heart. Not the physical heart, per se, but the essence of the living heart. Romantic writers have described a great sadness as a "broken heart to acknowledge a deep sense of grief." The ancient Egyptians pursued a more literal approach to assessing the empathetic and self-less nature of a person. At the time of death, they weighed the heart of the deceased and compared it to a feather. Hearts heavier than a feather were fed to the lions. Reasoning that feelings should be heart felt, the Egyptians thought the more love we had for others in the form of compassion and understanding, the lighter the heart would become.

These pure thoughts and feelings come from awareness that flows through prana, our vital force. This illustrates the importance of studying and practicing to regulate and balance our breath. The pranic field is both the essence of our coming into being and our resilience in the outside world. We need to care for this vital force as we would tend to a fire to avoid slipping into the place of fear and negativity.

This awareness that is developed from tending to our vital force can be applied to each and every one of our actions, and it will help us develop a skill to transform negative emotions into positive ones. Awareness is the witness. The more we don't identify with the object, the freer we are from negative emotions. So let's examine here the nature of negative emotions and their effect on our body.

When we polish our ego, we create the lens through which the light of pure awareness can shine and illuminate our entire being. Our emotion really arises from the image maker, ego. We become stressed when we perceive a threat to our existence. Perception is pure light, but when influenced by ego, it becomes clouded. So then we get a foggy view of "what is" when we look at something, depending on our memory impressions, as a stressor.

This threat is colored and influenced by our ego. We become stressed when an emotion arises, and we either try to change it or suppress it. For example, we may feel sad enough to cry but think it's a sign of weakness, so we try to hide our sadness and pretend we're not feeling it. Denying our emotions isn't healthy and over time creates blockages in our energy channels, especially the throat area. It stems from not knowing or trusting who we are and pretending to be something we aren't.

Each person spends a lifetime defending the ego, who they are (lawyer, artist, teacher, carpenter) and who they should be. We hide behind our persona, our personality. This persona develops based on feedback and conditioning in childhood. We wear a mask, never really getting access to our core being. So we ignore our emotions. When a child cries or becomes angry, he may be told, "Don't be angry; you shouldn't be angry. You shouldn't express your feelings. Don't cry; crying is shameful. Sensitivity is for girls." All of these messages create images of how we should feel and be, when, in fact, we suppress the natural expression.

This seems to happen to everyone on some level. We observe the expressions and the reactions of our parents or siblings. We become conditioned to behave a certain way based on our individuality and also perhaps what is and isn't accepted by the societal norm. As individuals, we each have our own perceptions depending on what we have in our storage facility called memory. That's why someone reacts to a situation while another remains calm.

IN TOUCH WITH HOW WE FEEL

Stress is suppressed emotion and changes our biochemistry. Deeply held emotions are in play when we layer our persona, as when we change our personality to act confident when we aren't; pretend we're okay when we're really angry; pretend to be happy for another person when feeling jealous; or do something so others will like us. Feelings generated in this way build heat and cause problems. That's not to imply that it's preferable to express our motives, animosity, or jealousy without any regard for the effect. I'm advocating that we acknowledge and understand the tendencies of our mind. Simply acknowledging and understanding their source will free us of the consequences of burying these emotions deep within our body.

All emotions have a shape and quality as tamas, rajas, and sattva. Tamasic emotions are stagnant, such as hatred and animosity, whereas anger and jealousy are more fiery in nature and are rajasic. Emotions of love, joy, and compassion are sattvic, wholesome, and pure. Any unresolved emotions crystallize; anything we experience leaves a footprint on our physical body and brain. Nothing happens in the mind that doesn't have its imprint on the brain.

Emotions that cause us to view ourselves as better or worse than others—such as animosity, hostility, anger, resentment, shame, and guilt—cause disruption of the limbic system in the brain, which means interference with cell repair mechanism and disruption of our healing ability. Our limbic system is the hub for sending out neurohormones involved in stress, which cause our hippocampus to shrink. It also causes areas in the limbic system to become more reactive. Negative emotions through the limbic system—our seat of emotional processes—can cause disruption of hormone levels and self-regulatory mechanisms. That can lead to a decline in homeostasis, leaving room for disease states to occur.

Conversely, the four emotions that the Buddhists revere—loving kindness, compassion, joy, and equanimity, the emotions stemming from pure awareness—actually cause the limbic centers in the brain to go into synchronicity, which accelerates our healing mechanism. The hypothalamus part of the limbic system is responsible for bringing homeostasis to the organism. When it receives positive input from other areas of the limbic system, it's able to balance and regulate the organism through the autonomic nervous system. So the synchronicity calls for all actions to be in process toward bringing homeostasis to the organism.

Positive emotions have a positive impact on the cellular mechanisms of the body. What we feed our mind by way of positive thoughts, impressions, and relationships sets in motion a return to balance.

Both Ayurvedic and Traditional Chinese Medicine acknowledge that unresolved emotions affect the body's organs. The lesson on energy channels taught us that they must be open to maintain flow. Our negative emotions take action on these channels by blocking them, giving rise to theories that unresolved anger stores in the liver, hate in the gallbladder, and worry in the kidney nephron.

Such thinking could seem odd to an allopathic practitioner, but the connection is obvious to those who have worked with their body and breath. We know that when we're fearful, our body reacts. A tense mind can create a tense lower back. Always remember that our body is indeed a crystallization of our mind. And emotions are part of our mind field.

Positive emotions help heal the body, as confirmed by a significant amount of research. Negative emotions take on the attributes of poison by slowly affecting our physical body. It's known that positive emotions help the nervous system to send signals to its respective endocrine organs, which in turn secrete hormones like oxytocin and endorphins—the body's natural, feel-good chemicals that strengthen immunity. An entire field of study with the tongue-twisting name, *psychoneuroimmunology*, investigates the effect of our thoughts, feelings, and emotions on our resilience by examining the immune system, the brain, and their signaling pathways.

We must also consider that once the body becomes tired or overstressed, it's difficult to have positive emotional balance. The mind ultimately creates disharmony in the body, and when the body becomes out of sync with its natural rhythm, it affects the emotional state. My experience provides a good example. I worked with a client who was overworked and extremely tired. Ellen was dealing with many family issues, including a son who was having much difficulty. She contacted me, saying she had been diagnosed with chronic anxiety and depression that was causing cognitive decline. Ellen was a woman in her later years, but after assessment of her symptoms (not her labels), we saw that her adrenals were taxed and her body was exhibiting lethargy, a symptom of fatigue. Her mind was cloudy. Over the course of eight weeks, we worked with nutrients and homeopathic remedies to restore balance to Ellen's digestive system, as well as her adrenals. She saw results within 10 days and continued to restore over the eight-week period.

I offer this example because it shows that the body and mind complex have to be looked at as one unit. It's much more challenging to work with the mind directly. We can't rationalize anxiety. It's far easier and more accessible to work with the body since it does indeed mirror the mind. Ultimately, the source of all our emotions is seeded in the desires springing from the primitive urges.

COOL THE GREAT EMOTIONAL CONUNDRUM

How do we transform negative emotions into positive ones? Emotions flow from the four fountains: food, sleep, sex, and self-preservation—and these are the root of all our desires. When our desires aren't satisfied by our "getting what we want" and we aren't trained to deal with a situation, we have a temper tantrum, which creates a negative emotion, such as anger, frustration, irritation, animosity, lust, jealousy, or envy. The solution isn't difficult: Learn to identify the source of the emotion. You can begin when you feel a negative emotion by asking yourself, "What do I want here?" Then you can explore the reason. Possible answers might be "to feel better about myself," "to feel important," or "to be acknowledged." When identified, we can decide that we don't want to engage and tell ourselves "not today." By practicing the "not today" response, we move along, as emotions do, rather than suppress or not acknowledge them.

On the other hand, when we do indeed get what we (*think*) we want, it lays the foundation for another set of emotions, such as pride and attachment, which leads to greed, wanting still more, and possible jealousy if we feel someone has more. We can see how the emotion—that which literally creates a motion—can lead to going in the direction of total imbalance. Since we've identified with this outside influence to make us feel good, we develop attachment to it. That leads to other emotions, because then we fear someone will take what we have—perhaps our security or our job—so we claim ownership of things that cause us to protect and defend what we've acquired. Now we see that this drives the root of our original desire deeper and wider. Our perception has lost track of the inner light of awareness, and ego has created many images that lead us to the darkness of negative emotions.

We can say that the two sources of emotions are desire and ego. The latter is our image maker that identifies with all the objects of the sensory world. The ego mistakenly believes it's the true nature or pure awareness. No humble rumblings here.

Emotions can be powerful transformative energy sources, but how can we harness our emotions? Those that serve as a positive power source are love, joy, and tranquility. Can we cultivate these and not fall prey to the negative influences of desire and the ego? To cultivate positive emotions is a practice in itself, requiring that we have an open heart, free of any worries and follies. Getting to the heart of the matter requires us to learn to move away from the obstacles.

To create love we must learn to give away and have no expectations. That's not to say that we give away all our essentials for day-to-day living. We simply practice that anything we *do* give is given with the intention of not expecting anything in return. A simple example is when you do someone a favor, you do it without expecting anything in return.

To create joy, we must change our perception and become observers. This is what we learn when we meditate. Many of us identify with our body or our brain. Or our job title or our disease label. What if we were to step back and ask ourselves who's doing the thinking, who's doing the breathing, and who's the one who keeps us alive as we sleep at night? As we learn to view things without likes and dislikes, we become joyful. Our likes and dislikes stain the fabric of our deepest essence that lies within the heart of everything and everyone.

We should start to pay attention to our mind chatter when we perceive something. Let the light of pure awareness shine through us, and our perception will be pure without the fogginess created from our likes and dislikes. To make the tranquil mind required to get to the core, we need self-acceptance that comes from meditation. Self-acceptance is part of what transpires when we put our likes and dislikes in the innocuous background. It really doesn't matter what we like and dislike; we just accept what is and move on.

PRACTICE LOOSE LIVING TO PROMOTE RELAXATION

Relaxation is the pathway to remain calm and ultimately work with our emotional health. Relaxation comes from the root "lax," which means "to loosen up." Athletes and thinkers agree: "You've got to loosen up your body and mind" if you want to be successful. Relaxation occurs at several levels not confined to muscles or mood: the physical and emotional body, and also mental and spiritual relaxation.

We can learn to manage our emotions by asking the question, "What is it that I want?" The awareness that springs from such a practice will cause profound results. We can manage our response with balanced breathing that begins with diaphragmatic breathing. But what can we do with the physical body, since that seems to be the most direct way to reach the deep roots of our emotional nature? You will recall that the yoga practice, called *agnisara,* works to regulate the physical body toward homeostasis by increasing digestive capacity. It also functions with our emotional nature.

Agnisara literally means "energizing the solar system," but here the solar system refers to the interconnection of the psychological and physiological processes that control our physical and mental digestion, so it's extremely useful in working with the emotional body. It, too, is a core foundation practice that, with consistency, will help massage internal organs and their associated chakras, resulting in cleansing and energizing our body and purifying our mind. Purification here is opening the energy channels by releasing stored impressions and associations that create emotional obstacles. In this way, we start to cultivate emotional alignment.

All these suggestions, combined with meditation, the topic of our next lesson, support the foundation for stable emotions.

"No one succeeds without effort.
Those who succeed owe their
success to perseverance."
—RAMANA MAHARSHI

Review

TRUTH

Desires from the four fountains feed our emotions.

OBSTACLE

Being unaware of the true source of our emotions.

EXIT STRATEGY

Learn to reach and harness our emotional world.

FACTS

- ❖ Our body is a crystallization of our mind.

- ❖ Ego is our image maker.

- ❖ Desire feeds emotions.

- ❖ Healthy emotions change our biochemistry.

Path *of* Practice

"Mind is indeed the Builder ... what is held in the act of mental vision becomes a reality in the material experience. We are gradually builded to that image created within our own mental being."

—EDGAR CAYCE

 JOURNAL ACTIVITY

Purpose:

Finding the connection between your emotions and the surrounding environment (people, circumstances) is a skill that helps you discover your perception.

Technique:

1. Keep track of your emotional fluctuations. When you start to see what situations cause you to react more emotionally than others, you can backtrack and detect the source.

2. You can use a term that has been extremely useful in my personal life—"not today"—a simple but powerful statement when the mind wants to go south and you're meant to go east.

3. Start to discover what circumstances feed your anger, jealousy, irritability, sadness, or even cause you to feel anxious. For example: Do you tend to pick up the mood of the person to whom you're talking? What do you need to do to keep from being affected by your environment? Do you have strategies for remaining unaffected by your environment?

Core Practice
"Bee Breath" (*Bhramari*)

"Bee Breath" (*Bhramari*) is a powerful breathing practice that balances the autonomic nervous system. The mind becomes absorbed in the sound, thus, negating any of the mental scripts that may be playing in the background. By adjusting the exhalation, it produces a calming effect. *Bhramari* practice can have a profound effect on stabilizing anxious emotions.

Purpose:

To calm and harmonize the mind. It's one of the best breathing exercises to release the mind of anger, agitation, frustration, or anxiety.

Technique:

1. Sit with the head, neck, and trunk aligned on a cushion, chair, bench, or a bolster. Place the index fingers softly in the ears, with the other fingers lightly clenched. Here the arms extend out horizontally.

2. Keep the mouth closed with your teeth slightly parted. Inhale slowly and steadily.

3. On the exhale, make a humming sound for the duration of the entire exhalation. The exhale and sound should be smooth, with no jerks or pauses. The awareness here is to hear the vibration in the head, not necessarily a loud sound. Notice how the vibration feels on the tongue, teeth, and sinuses. Feel the entire brain vibrate.

4. Repeat again. Inhale and then exhale, and make the humming-bee sound. Do this for 3–6 rounds. And on the last one, don't hum. Just see if you can hear the sound in your head. Keep the eyes closed for some time. Observe the sensations in the body and the quietness within.

5. Option: Practice with adding *shanmukhi mudra* (the closing of the six gates), here gates refering to two eyes, two ears, nose and the mouth. Block the external input of the senses by using the thumbs to push on the tragus of each ear so that it closes the ear canal. (That is the bump that extends from the ear canal.) The second fingers resting gently on the eyelids to close the eyes. The third fingers resting on each side of the nose, the

fourth and fifth fingers encircling the upper and lower lip to close the mouth. Practice bhramari for 3-6 rounds.

Note: This practice is more a meditational practice than a breathing practice. You can follow this with meditation.

"We are not going in circles;
we are going upwards.
The path is a spiral; we have
already climbed many steps."
—HERMAN HESSE

It's a Matter of Practice

We have arrived at the final lesson, which will open the door to gain access to our healing force. Each and every one of us must take responsibility for our own healing and life. No one is with us when we come in, and no one is with us to escort us out. We must trust and know the journey.

Mastery of meditation and its practice remove the mystery of knowing our life's journey. Meditation gives us something that no outside force can offer. It introduces us to our Self. The regular practice of meditation means we can be solid like the earth, flow like life-giving water, radiate like fire, and carry nothing, as if in weightless space.

There is much discussion about mindfulness, but only when combined with focus does mindfulness take us beyond the sensory realm into a place of pure awareness. In this lesson, we understand how meditation puts us in touch with our perceptions and feelings.

PUT RELAXATION INTO ACTION

In traditional cultures throughout history, the mind and body have been viewed as inseparable entities. Meditation was the tool used to get access to the mind-body-spirit matrix and to allow for greater awareness. Meditation has been traditional in the East, but its profile only was raised in the 1960s within the context of Western science when the mechanics of meditation and its effects were the subject of intense research. Scientists recorded the changes in practitioners' physical functions, such as blood pressure, heart rate, respiratory function, as well as function of the brain and its relation to thoughts and emotions.

In the early 1970s, meditation was touted as a relaxation technique that could alleviate physical stress. Although the concept of a "relaxation response" was convenient as an initial explanation for what was happening in the meditative state, later work showed that what was happening physiologically was much more complex than a decrease in heart and respiratory rate.

By the 1990s, meditation was becoming accepted in *medicine*, and it was incorporated into stress reduction programs offered at many traditional health care facilities. One well-known example is the mindfulness program organized by Jon Kabat-Zinn, PhD, an author, professor, and expert associated with the Stress Reduction Clinic at the University of Massachusetts Medical Center. Today, ancient healing traditions and modern medicine alike recognize meditation as a proven technique for restoring balance and vitality to the overstressed mind.

As I advise people in search of studies for validation, "Study your own mind, become your own laboratory. Only this data is lasting and pure."

The word "meditation" comes from the root word "medi," which means "to attend to." Just as a medical practitioner attends to a patient, the practice of meditation involves using any number of awareness techniques to attend to quieting the mind and relaxing the body. Concentration practices found within Transcendental Meditation and mindfulness meditation are perhaps the best known. No matter what style or technique we use, in all styles we sit quietly, witnessing internal thoughts and external stimuli without getting caught up in them. This is why meditation is used in most stress reduction programs. People also use prayer, contemplation, visualization, and hypnosis for stress reduction, but meditation is different.

WE SEARCH OUTSIDE FOR HEALING WITHIN

It's common for us to seek answers to healing outside of ourselves, when in fact the source of our healing is inside us. The reason is that our spiritual technology hasn't developed along with our physical technology. Though many inventions assist us in living, only attention to the spiritual aspects of our being can prevent our "progress" from becoming a destructive force. Spirituality—

recognition of the life force that lies at the core of all living entities—must become the foundation for our abundance and development if we're to evolve and mature; indeed, if we're to survive at all. There's only one way out and it's in. That's where our wholeness resides.

Viewing Eastern and Western disciplines as interlocking allows us to examine life as a whole. The vision offered through this approach is what it takes to live in a hyper culture and, at the same time, connect with the inner core of our being. We term this "holistic medicine" or "mind-body medicine."

Focusing on individual parts of ourselves doesn't heal us, because these parts can't be successfully extricated from the whole being. Health is a dynamic state that includes mental and spiritual well-being, not merely a lack of symptoms. We can begin our journey to health only by acknowledging and honoring the dynamic interrelatedness of our exquisitely designed human system. This isn't so easy to get our head around, but simple breath and simple posture is the start. In this profound, ancient form of restorative therapy, our greatest counsel comes from our cushion. As we'll see, in meditation our practice allows us to travel inward—and upward—toward our inner source of self-healing.

The biochemistry of healing starts with our perceptions and feelings. And meditation puts us in touch with that. We each have a body that too often is looked on as an entity separate from the mind. We depend on breath, which usually goes without notice. We each have a mind that isn't at all understood by Western science—a mind that, in fact, is most of the time mistaken for the brain. And we each have a soul that, when revealed, gives us a glimpse of its pure brilliance.

Healing requires addressing the biochemical, physiological, and psychological aspects of our total being. When disconnected from the center of our being, we begin to lose access to this powerful healing system. When we look outside for the healing power that's within, we create a disconnect and disease results.

The disconnect is heightened when we fail to find the origin of our problem and its symptoms, relying instead on the promises made on behalf of a pill or potion. True healing, on the other hand, results from the ability to look inside and trust our own intelligence to determine the root of what ails us. Through awareness training, we're able to locate the root and often resolve the issue.

The next time you get a twinge of anxiety, stop and ask yourself, "From where is this coming?" Here's a hint: Anxiety is the result of looking ahead in time and reflects our imaginings of the future. Depression is looking back and reflects our regrets of the past and our inability to digest our experiences. Hence, we need to learn to be CALM. Being aware in this way and paying attention to its relevance to our circumstance in the moment remedies our disconnect. It puts us on the path toward assuming the natural role as our own powerful healer.

REMIND YOURSELF TO BE MINDFUL

Mindfulness is a form of practice that teaches the practitioner to be in the moment while observing sensory stimuli and thoughts that arise. If we think of a camera with a wide-angle lens—one that takes in the panoramic view—that's mindfulness as taught in Western view. The concept to think about here is that our sensory mind, called *manas*, is endless. In other words, it will keep on searching for data since that's its job. If we learn to practice mindfulness by bringing it into focus, we can recognize the target of that mindfulness. In other words, our mind will be able to go deeper into our unconscious and reach the source. Bringing mindfulness into focus is like using a short-angle lens. We still are being mindful but we narrow the view.

We may think we're too aware of our thoughts as we plan or daydream, ruminate on the past or perhaps fret about the future; but meditation awareness is different. This comes as a surprise to many students. They have the misconception that meditation involves a mind that's thought-free.

Thoughts are very bashful. The moment we become aware of them, they begin to dissolve. The Eastern understanding is that only in relaxation can we be truly aware, and vice versa. By learning to focus our awareness—letting go of thoughts and images that are of no interest, while allowing those of interest—we get access to our healing potential and revitalize ourselves.

Once we can witness the succession of thoughts wandering in the mind, the next skill to develop is the ability to be non-attached to these fleeting constructs. We simply remain the witness. Over time we develop the skill to call back thought patterns so they can be observed and contemplated. A still body and smooth breath must be maintained throughout this process.

Health is a dynamic state that includes physical,
emotional, mental, and spiritual well-being,
not merely a lack of symptoms or disease.

Deciding which thoughts are helpful and which are not is a skill unto itself, but it's one we can cultivate. A master once said, "By learning to witness, and then learning to inspect individual thoughts for their useful versus not useful qualities, we become free from the control of unconscious thought patterns and move ever closer to the experience of the deep center of consciousness. The ability to inspect individual thoughts is a skill, not a method, and is crucial for advancing in meditation."

This ability to bring back and inspect thought patterns allows us to cease being dragged around by old impressions and habits of the mind—feeling scared and vulnerable when criticized in our adult lives because we didn't feel unconditional love as children, habitually replaying conversations or encounters, or routinely worrying about what we fear may happen tomorrow, next month, next year. Often we're unaware of our thought patterns and how they drive our habits. A feeling followed by a thought is triggered, and we don't know why or how. Then we behave, think, or feel in habitual ways, again with little comprehension of how or why. In this way, we can easily be unconsciously led to actions and speech that we regret. Meditation allows us to get access to these thought patterns so they no longer rule us.

After we discriminate between helpful and unhelpful thought patterns, we can intentionally reinforce positive and useful thoughts through willpower. In that way, we can transform those thoughts into actions or new habits of thinking.

Feeding and nourishing helpful thoughts is a learned, cultivated, practiced behavior. The root skill is to promote the positive. We direct willpower, or what is termed *sankalpashakti*, toward turning positive thoughts into action. Here, the metabolism of the mind field comes into play.

We previously explored the balanced, integrated four functions of mind. The sensory mind (manas) is trained; it serves its purpose but isn't in charge. The ego (ahamkara, the image maker) is clear and doesn't cloud the lens of the wise and discriminating buddhi. Our stored memories and thought patterns (chitta) are now accessible for introspection from our unconscious mind. *(You may find it helpful now to review Lesson 9 to solidify your understanding of this balance.)*

And what do we do with the negative that doesn't promote growth and well-being? Nothing. Not easy for many of us, I know, but with practice this *can* be done. We observe the unhelpful thoughts but do not wrestle or wrangle with them. By not engaging, we allow them to pass more quickly. Over time, as we consistently, consciously refuse to engage with unhelpful thoughts, they lose their power to allure us from a calm and focused place. They are diminished. A regular meditation practice, in which the negative is not engaged, offers a great reward—the kind of self-control and poise that extends from meditation time into all aspects of life.

When we remain calm, we are able to determine that a situation or thought is "not useful to us." And since balance is one result of a meditation or relaxation practice, we could find our Self remaining indifferent to even useful thoughts. Our perceptions now begin to change, eliminating the need to take so much of life's experiences as personal. All of this manifests as a result of our increased awareness of both our sensory mind and ego.

Remaining calm allows us to consciously respond with the integrated four functions of mind rather than react—out of fear, ego, or stored memory impressions. This calmness doesn't mean we will be emotion-free; rather, it allows us to maintain positive emotions due to our increased awareness. Instead of having an emotional response that arises and stays with us for an extended period of time, we learn to have an emotional response that quickly fades away as we observe it. With time this kind of response will become our default reaction.

As we practice, take note of how long it takes to have what I call a "temper tantrum" and let go of a negative thought or experience. This will demonstrate the growing strength of our mindfield.

Self-control is achieved in slow stages; it very rarely is achieved all at once. When we develop the skill of not being disturbed, we can enjoy being unaffected in any situation. It's important to focus on progress and practice, not perfection, because we can't expect instant. We aren't striving to *act* calm or to *appear* undisturbed. We practice remaining calm without taking action. This is powerful in and of itself. Over time, we're strengthening our ability to *be* calm.

Non-attachment, the quality of not being disturbed, is a critical skill in advanced meditation, in which accumulated, practiced skills function in concert to help us reach this goal. Cultivating these skills, step by step, always with compassion for our selves, is the goal rather than reaching the "summit" of non-attachment.

"Tomorrow's battle is won during today's practice."
—Japanese Proverb

PRACTICE MAKES PERFECT MEDITATION

As I've discussed in depth, we can all benefit from a systematic relaxation and meditation practice. I know of no better nor beneficial way for brain, body, and mind to reach homeostasis than through these practices. But many of the participants in retreats pronounce themselves unable to meditate, saying they've tried and feel like failures. Often their inability to meditate is linked to the misconception that meditation is about ridding the mind of all thoughts. Once they practice relaxation on a regular basis, their mind chatter becomes less of an issue. Preparing the mind and body is essential to practice.

While the components I set forth here aren't complicated, they can make the difference between reaping the benefits of a meditation practice and throwing up one's hands in frustration. Remember that the practices in the preceding lessons of this book prepare the mind for meditation. Also, we must acknowledge that meditation isn't easy. Understanding the science behind preparing the mind and body for meditation will help in leading you to a successful meditation practice.

The obstacles to meditating include: uncomfortable posture; physical, emotional, and mental tension; illness, which creates discomfort in the body and radiates to the mind; fatigue; and having eaten too much or too little food before practicing. As with any new habit we hope to establish, we need a system to make progress. The systematic approach described here, should enable us to overcome many obstacles that cause an unsteady or restless mind. We'll find a posture that allows us to be comfortable and steady. We'll learn to breathe correctly so we can relax the body and sit comfortably. And we'll follow a sequence that creates a *habit* of steadiness and stability so we can experience beneficial results.

The practices that I teach in this country and internationally are based on traditional yoga meditation. The purpose is to train all levels of our being—senses, body, breath, nervous system, emotions, and mind—in order to reach the power of healing within the soul. The sequence has been developed to train the body and mind from the outside to inside and has been established to facilitate this process. It is as follows:

1. **Steadiness in posture**—the ability to sit with the head, neck, and spine aligned to promote stability of mind and body.

2. **Diaphragmatic breathing**—the skill of breathing while using the diaphragm muscle in order to balance the nervous system.

3. **Systematic relaxation**—the act of sequentially freeing the body of all levels of tension: physical, mental, emotional, and spiritual.

4. **Refined breathing (breath awareness)**—the practice of even inhalation and exhalation, without pauses or jerks; if the breath is calm, the mind is calm; whatever the breath is doing, the mind will follow.

5. **Mindfulness in Focus**—the act of becoming an objective observer when a thought arises and giving full attention to a symbol or word. Here we use the mantra "So-Ham." Pronounced "so-hum."

 Step 1

Establish a Firm Seat

Steadiness of our mind begins with steadiness of our posture. A still body lends itself to a still mind. With this in mind, we need to establish a steady and firm seat for our practice. To maintain the geometry of the posture, think of a tetrahedron (pyramid). The simplest of three-dimensional structures, it's made of four triangular surfaces. If we think of our body as seated within this pyramid structure, our thighs will be in alignment with our knees; our spine will be erect; and the tips of our knees will be in line with the top of our head—forming a triangle.[32]

 Step 2

Establish diaphragmatic breathing

Diaphragmatic breathing is both energizing and relaxing. Focus and breath are the two key principles that support a relaxed mind. This is the simplest and most profound way to learn systematic relaxation. By focusing one's attention on the breath, you get the physiological benefits as well as the systematic training of the mind. (*See Lesson 3 for a review.*)

Step 3

Relax systematically

Relaxation, the third step in systematic meditation, is the doorway to meditation. We begin by bringing our awareness to our head and travel systematically downward through the body from our head to our toes and from our toes to our head, releasing any tension.

Step 4

Refine your breath (breath awareness)

Paying attention to the air leaving and entering your nostrils is a great focusing tool and the most basic breathing practice. This allows for the development of heightened sensitivity and inner awareness, and acts as a barometer for our meditation practice.

Step 5

Focus on mantra (infinite vibration)

Mantras help clear and stabilize the mind so the highest levels of being could be experienced. Religious, spiritual, and meditative traditions throughout time and around the world have used such words and sounds, variously known as mantras, prayers, affirmations, or incantations. The "*so-hum*" (or *soham*) mantra is natural and universal. *So* is the natural sound of the breath on inhalation, and *ham* sounds like *hum,* the natural sound of the breath on exhaling.

These are the components—posture, breath, relaxation, breath awareness, and mantra—of bringing mindfulness into focus. It's now time to practice them.

Review

TRUTH

Look within or be without.

OBSTACLE

Stress disconnects us from our healing center.

EXIT STRATEGY

Meditation introduces us to our Self.

FACTS

❖ Meditation can liberate the mind from distraction.

❖ Practice is the path to a calm and focused mind.

❖ Health includes both mental & spiritual well-being.

❖ Awareness is the key to self-transformation.

Path *of* Practice

"The first step in meditation is concentration, and you can attain that depth of concentration if you train yourself. Never give up! Accept meditation as part of your life, just as you eat, sleep, and do other things; make it a prominent goal to have a calm mind, to have a one-pointed mind, to have a tranquil mind. Do not give that up."

—SWAMI RAMA

 JOURNAL ACTIVITY

Purpose:

To help you establish a systematic meditation practice that will gradually bring you from the body to the more subtle realms of the mind.

Technique:

1. Record the time of day and length of each session for each entry.

2. Describe your experience. Include what is challenging and the adjustments you make to address these difficulties. For example, you may find it challenging to decide when to do your practice.

3. Note what becomes easier over time. Look for changes in your daily life, such as your responses to stress, provoking situations or people, for instance, or your energy levels and sleep patterns.

4. Write down the positive, nurturing thoughts that occur during your sessions and counter any negative ones with more nourishing ideas.

Core Practices
Meditation on the Ajna Chakra

The seat of the mind is the eyebrow center, the *ajna chakra*. Bringing our attention to the ajna chakra allows us to control our mind more easily than focusing on other areas, such as heart center (*anahata chakra*). With consistent practice, the practitioner balances the energy in this region and finds that the mind's wandering tendencies diminish, opening the door to meditation, mantra, and intuition. The practice yields a sense of calm, focus, and joy.

Purpose:

To put together what we've learned and bring mindfulness into focus by concentrating on the eyebrow center.

Technique:

1. Sit with the body aligned. Imagine a gold thread up the center of the spine holding the body erect and steady. You can be in a chair or on the floor. If on the floor, fold the legs in a gentle way, making sure the spine is erect. You may want to sit on a pillow and rotate the hips slightly forward.

2. Begin by sitting with the eyes closed. Recall the imaginary thread up the center of the spine and out the top of the head, holding you steady. Now scan the body to help get rid of any tension that may exist. Start at the forehead, and then scan the face (eyelids, cheeks, corners of the mouth, and chin). Then mentally go to the neck, shoulders, arms, torso, buttocks, legs,

and toes. Relax by breathing into each area and then exhaling all tension. Return to the head.

3. Next, practice breath awareness. Bring your attention to the point between the two nostrils. Pay attention to the coolness of air as it enters, and its warmth upon leaving. Be there for a few moments. Then bring your attention to the point just above the space between the eyebrows, or to the point between the two breasts. (If you tend to be overly emotional, go to the space just above the two eyebrows.) Be there, and breathe into and out of the space. Upon inhalation, repeat silently the sound "*so*," and upon exhalation, repeat silently the sound "*hum*." *So-hum.*

4. During this time, watch the thoughts and see how the body reacts to them. It's important to observe them without judgment, keeping in mind that you're the observer of the thoughts and you're not the thoughts. Working with mind may bring up new levels of awareness of stored impressions and memories.

5. Don't try to stop them, just gently bring your focus back to the sound *so-hum*. When you feel ready, gently bring your focus back to the point between the two nostrils and breathe more deeply as you bring your attention back to the body. Then, gently bring your hands up in front of the eyes without touching the face. Slowly open the eyes.

6. Begin with just 5 or 10 minutes; the goal is focus, not length of time. As you progress, you'll practice for longer periods of time.

Note: *If you're new to meditation, it might be a good idea to find a teacher with whom you resonate to guide you through your practice. You may benefit from listening to a CD to help get you started.*

*"Most people believe the mind to be a mirror,
more or less accurately reflecting the world outside them,
not realizing, on the contrary, that the mind is
itself the principal element of creation."*
—RABINDRANATH TAGORE

Live in the World
but Remain Above

The search for happiness pervades the human condition, but living in the world continually sidetracks us through exposure to its chaos. A solid foundation in mind and body can serve as a shield to feeling the pervasive pain and suffering. We can work to discover our inner illumination by understanding the forces that bind us as well as the nature of obstacles to our goal of organic happiness. While everyone seeks a place of tranquility and happiness—often subconsciously—we choose individual roads. The path I have mapped in this book's 12 lessons points inward to our deepest Self.

We needn't be willing victims of our environment if we identify its dangers and develop a healthy approach. While toxic relationships and troublesome situations may not yield to quick fixes, we can learn to live in our environment through practicing being unaffected. Free from the vines of attachment, we then can move into a place of calm and contentment. Keep in mind that we learn to know our Self—our strengths and weaknesses—by engaging in the world, and only then can we begin to remove our no longer hidden problems.

"This yoga should be practiced with firm
determination and perseverance,
without any mental reservation or doubts."
—BHAGAVAD GITA

To be part of the outer world and not be disturbed, distracted, or stupefied by it, remaining calm and focused, requires mastery over our Self. We'll need to let go of our attachment to our likes, dislikes, and desires by having command over what fuels these drives—usually our fears. The practices we've learned through this book can offer building blocks for a foundation on which we can establish self-mastery.

Practice, practice, practice to discover who we are, and surely we'll build the self-confidence and inner strength to move through the obstacles that have and will bar the way. Know that obstacles will be ever present, as they're a natural part of being in the world.

The ancient scriptures in yoga science teach that the most

valuable life skill is the ability to live in this world and not be affected by it. Yet this may be one of our greatest challenges, because non-attachment and practice are key to living in the world without becoming disturbed by what takes place around us. This is the only way we can endure with peace and harmony despite the chaos around us.

Attachment results in becoming disturbed, distracted, and depressed. It's the result of relying on something outside of ourselves for enjoyment and happiness; it's something we expect in return for our efforts, our love, and our devotion. How much disharmony we may experience can be related to our level of attachment.

Don't confuse "non-attachment" with "not loving" someone or something, when in fact the opposite is true. Remaining non-attached gives us the capacity to love because we can let go. We become so reliant on our beliefs—likes and dislikes—that we lose our capacity to love and struggle with what we *want to be*.

When we practice non-attachment, we learn to become the witness. To be an observer in life requires that we first have the awareness to see *what is*, followed by the understanding of the forces behind what we're witnessing. This requires great practice but is nothing more than watching and having the skills to recognize what really is taking place.

This is where the practice of meditation is helpful. We learn to drop into the role of being an observer even if we become involved in what's happening in the world. When we have the skill, we can remain non-attached to the outcome.

But this is where most of us encounter the conundrum: We

feel sad when the outcome is not what we want and happy when it's what we want. We identify so intensely with our likes and dislikes that we never can be totally happy. It's that simple.

I believe diligent practice can empower us to dilute that age-old conflict by making us aware so we can position our mind field.

Ultimately, when we know our purpose in life and keep our focus on it, we achieve sustainable happiness. When we surrender and trust in ourselves, we gain access to our spiritual heart. Trust builds love, devotion, and selfless service. Only then can we heal ourselves.

We begin by working with our attitudes to open the heart for our access. Chanting, selfless service, and devotion can be helpful, as well as adopting general attitudes.

When confronted with a negative situation that we must rise above, I've found these techniques valuable:

- Look for the opportunity in everything. If we're breathing, we can be grateful for the opportunity to do something about our life.
- Remove likes and dislikes from our vocabulary. This will give us access to everlasting peace and happiness.
- Take responsibility and don't complain or blame others for our situation. We often get caught up in this scenario. We blame others only because we can't face our issues. When we take responsibility for our own thoughts and actions, we no longer depend on outside influences to determine how we feel.

✪ Form relationships based on love—non-attachment—not need. We ask, "Why am I in this relationship?" First we assess our relationship with our Self. That relationship will mirror our relationship with others.

✪ Serve others. Do for others. Through generosity to others, we give to ourselves. This is the ultimate in practicing love. When we learn to love and give unconditionally, we're no longer affected by the world. We have learned to live in the world and remain above.

The Yoga of Mind, Medicine, and Healing is a beginners' path for spiritual seekers—those who want to make this life a journey toward fulfillment. The spiritual head of the Himalayan Institute, Pandit Rajmani Tigunait, PhD, has expressed a beautifully simple statement: "Human beings are an island of excellence."

In accordance with yoga science, we can hold onto two-thirds of our Self without it being engaged outside of us, but the remaining one-third must interact with the environment. The potential for that influence to create imbalance is constant.

I believe we can bring our mind into focus and heal ourselves, even in the presence of an increasingly uncertain world. We absolutely can do this. There is no mystery when there is mastery.

In closing, I offer the sage words of Swami Rama: "*In yoga, knowledge is not the result of strain. It emerges from consistent practice. Practice promotes constant awareness. With attention, you can enjoy the world.*"

Feeling Good Matters

Footnotes

1. Bolam JP, Hanley JJ, Booth Pac, Bevan MD. "Synaptic organization of the basal ganglia." *Journal of Anatomy* 2000;196 (Pt 4):527-542.

2. Benson, Herbert. *The Relaxation Response.* New York: Harper-Collins, 1975 (2001).

3. Ghershon, Michael D. *The Second Brain.* New York: Harper Collins, 1998.

4. Culligan, Eamonn P., Marchesi, Julian R., Hill, Colin, Sleator, Roy. D. "Mining the human gut microbiome for novel stress resistance genes." *Gut Microbes.* July 1, 2012; 3(4): 394-397.

5. Selhub, Eva M., Logan, Alan C., Bested, Alison, C. "Fermented foods, microbiota, and mental health: Ancient practice meets nutritional psychiatry." *Journal of Physiological Anthropology,* 2014; 33(1): 2.

6. Metchnikoff, E., Chalmers, M. P. *The prolongation of life. Optimistic studies.* (New York & London: GP Putnam & Sons, 1910). 96p.

7. Mayer, EA. "Gut feelings: the emerging biology of gut-brain communication." *Nature Reviews Neuroscience,* 2011; July 13; 12(8):453-66.

8. Logan, A.C., Katzman, M.; Major Depressive Disorder: Probiotics May Be An Adjuvant Therapy. *Medical Hypothesis,* 2005; 64 (3): 533-8.

9. Chia, Mantak. *Awakening Healing Energy through the Tao,* Aurora Press, 1983; pp. 21-28.

10. Tilisch, Kristen. Labus, J., Kilpatrick, L., Jiang, Z., Stains, J., Ebrat, B. Guyonnet, D., Legrain-Raspaud, S., Trotin, B., Naliboff, B., Mayer, E., A. "Consumption of fermented milk product with probiotic modulates brain activity." *Gastroenterology,* 2013; 144(7), 1394-1401.

11. Schonfeld, P, and Reiser, G. "Why does the brain metabolism not favor burning of fatty acids to provide energy? Reflections on disadvantage of the use of free fatty acids as a fuel for brain." (REVIEW) *Journal of Cerebral Blood Flow & Metabolism,* 2013; 33: 1493–1499.

12. Ragozzino, ME. "Hippocampal acetylcholine release during memory testing in rats: augmentation glucose." *Proceeding of the National Academy of Sciences,* 1996 vol. 93 no. 10. p 4693-4698.

13. Simopoulos AP. "The importance of the omega-6/omega-3 fatty acid ratio in cardiovascular disease and other chronic diseases." *Experimental Biology and Medicine,* 2008 June; 233 (6):674-88. Epub 2008 April 11.

14. Conklin SM, Gianaros PJ, Brown SM, Yao JK, Hariri AR, Manuck SB, Muldoon MF. "Long-chain omega-3 fatty acid intake is associated positively with corticolimbic gray matter volume in healthy adults." *Neuroscience Letter*, 2007 June 29; 421(3):209-12.

15. Mozaffarian D, Katan MB, Ascherio A, Stampfer MJ, Willett WC. "Trans Fatty Acids and Cardiovascular Disease." *New England Journal of Medicine*, 354 (15): 1601–1613. April 2006. PMID 16611951.

16. Food and Nutrition Board, Institute of Medicine of the National Academies. "Dietary Reference Intakes for Energy, Carbohydrate, Fiber, Fat, Fatty Acids, Cholesterol, Protein and Amino Acids (Macronutrients)." *National Academies Press*, 2005; 504.

17. Sibille E, Su J, Leman S, LeGuisquet AM, Ibarguen-Vargas Y, Joeyen-Waldorf J, Glorioso C, Tseng GC, Pezzone M, Hen R, Belzung C. "Lack of serotonin 1B receptor expression leads to age-related motor dysfunction, early onset of brain molecular aging and reduced longevity." *Modern Psychiatry*, 2007; 12:1042–1056.

18. Meltzer CC, Reynolds CF III. "In vivo assessment of aging changes in serotonin function." *Neuropsychopharmacology*, 1999; 21:323–324.

19. Scherman D, Desnos C, Darchen F, Pollack P, Javoy-Agid F, Agid Y: "Striatal dopamine deficiency in Parkinson's disease: role of aging." *Annals of Neurology,* 1989; 26:551–557.

20. Wurtman RJ, Wurtman JJ, Regan MM, McDermott JM, Tsay RH, Breu JJ et al. "Effects of normal meals rich in carbohydrates or proteins on plasma tryptophan and tyrosine ratios." *American Journal of Clinical Nutrition,* January 2003; 77(1):128-32.

21. Raichle, ME., Gusnard, DA. "Appraising the brain's energy budget." *Proceedings of the National Academy of Sciences,* August 6, 2002; vol. 99 no. 16 10237-10239.

22. Bayani Uttara, Ajay V. Singh, Paolo Zamboni, and R.T Mahajan. "Oxidative Stress and Neurodegenerative Diseases: A Review of Upstream and Downstream Antioxidant Therapeutic Options." *Current Neuropharmacology,* March 2009; 7(1): 65–74.

23. Rando, TA, Disatnik, MH, Yu, Y and Franco, A. "Muscle cells from mdx mice have an increased susceptibility to oxidative stress." *Neuromuscular Disorders,* 1998; 8:14-2.

24. Murphy, ME, and Kehrer, JP. "Oxidation state of tissue thiol groups and content of protein carbonyl groups in chickens with inherited muscular dystrophy." *Biochemical Journal,* 1989; 260: 359-64.

25. DeWeese, TL, Shipman, JM, Larrier, NA, Buckley, NM, Kidd, LR, Groopman, JD, Cutler, RG, te Riele, H, and Nelson, WG. "Mouse embryonic stem cells carrying one or two defective Msh2 alleles respond abnormally to oxidative stress inflicted by low-level radiation." *Proceedings of the National Academy of Sciences,* 1998; 95:11915-20.

26. Meyer, TE, Liang, HQ, Buckley, AR, Buckley, DJ, Gout, PW, Green, EH and Bode, AM. "Changes in glutathione redox cycling and oxidative stress response in the malignant progression of NB2 lymphoma cells." *International Journal of Cancer,* 1998; 77: 55-63.

27. Stadtman, ER and Berlett, BS. "Reactive oxygen-mediated protein oxidation in aging and disease." *Drug Metabolism Reviews,* 1998; 30:225-43.

28. Beckman, KB and Ames, BN. "The free radical theory of aging matures." *Physiological Reviews,* 1998; 78: 547-81.

29. *Merriam-Webster Dictionary,* 2014.

30. Sovik, Rolf, PsychD. *Moving Inward: The Journey to Meditation.* (Himalayan Institute Press, 2005); 156.

31. Pandit Rajmani Tigunait, Ph.D., *Secret of the Yoga Sutra. Samadhi Pada.* Himalayan Institute of Yoga Science and Philosophy, 2014.

32. Coulter, David. *Anatomy of Hatha Yoga.* Honesdale, PA: Body and Breath, 2001.

Additional Resources for Further Study

AYURVEDA

Frawley, D. (2000). *Ayurvedic Healing: A comprehensive guide* (2nd rev. and enl. ed.). Twin Lakes, Wisc. Lotus Press.

Frawley, D. and Vasant, L. (1986) *The Yoga of Herbs*. Lotus Press.

Frawley, D. (1997). *Ayurveda and the Mind: The healing of consciousness*. Lotus Press.

Lad, V. (1984) *Ayurveda: The Science of Self-Healing*. Lotus Press, Santa Fe, NM.

Svoboda, R. (1999). *Ayurveda for Women: A guide to vitality and health*. Devon: David & Charles.

Svoboda, R. (1989). *Prakruti: Your Ayurvedic Constitution*. Albuquerque, NM. GEOCOM.

Welch, C. (2011). *Balance your Hormones, Balance your Life: Achieving optimal health and wellness through Ayurveda, Chinese medicine, and western science*. Cambridge, MA: Da Capo Lifelong.

References

TRADITIONAL CHINESE MEDICINE

Beinfield, H. & Korngold, E. (1992). *Between Heaven and Earth: A guide to Chinese medicine.* New York. Ballantine Books.

Beinfield, H. & Korngold, E. (1992). *A Guide to Chinese Medicine.* New York. Ballantine Books.

Hammer, L. (1991). *Dragon Rises, Red Bird Flies: Psychology, energy & Chinese medicine.* Barrytown, N.Y. Station Hill Press.

Kaptchuk, T. (1983). *The Web that Has No Weaver: Understanding Chinese medicine.* New York. Congdon & Weed.

Veith, I. (1972). *Huang Ti nei ching su wên. The Yellow Emperor's Classic of Internal Medicine. Chapters 1-34* (New edition). Berkeley. University of California Press.

HOLISTIC HEALTH & NUTRITION

Ballentine, R. (2011). *Radical Healing: Integrating the world's great therapeutic traditions to create a new transformative medicine.* Himalayan Institute Press.

Bland, J. (2014). *The Disease Delusion: Conquering the causes of chronic illness for a healthier, longer, and happier life.* New York. Harper Wave.

Campbell, T. & Campbell, T. (2005). *The China Study: The most comprehensive study of nutrition ever conducted and the startling implications for diet, weight loss and long-term health.* Dallas, Tex.: BenBella Books.

Fallon, S. & Enig, M. (2001). *Nourishing Traditions: The cookbook that challenges politically correct nutrition and the diet dictocrats* (2nd rev. edition). Washington, DC: NewTrends Pub.

Gershon, M. (1998). *The Second Brain: The scientific basis of gut instinct and a groundbreaking new understanding of nervous disorders of the stomach and intestine.* New York, NY: HarperCollins.

Greenblatt, J. (2012) *A Culinary Journey: A personal voyage into the world of herbs, spices & vegetarian cuisine.* Carlsbad, CA: Aperion Books.

Haas, E., & Levin, B. (2006). *Staying Healthy with Nutrition: The complete guide to diet and nutritional medicine* (21st-century edition). Berkeley: Celestial Arts.

Lipton, B. (2005). *The Biology of Belief: Unleashing the power of consciousness, matter and miracles.* Santa Rosa, CA: Mountain of Love/Elite Books.

Pert, C. (1997). *Molecules of Emotion: Why you feel the way you feel.* New York, NY: Scribner.

Price, W. and Price P. (2009) *Nutrition and Physical Degeneration, Nutrition.* (8th edition).

Taylor, S. (2007) *The Vital Energy Program.* CD Set. Sounds True.

Taylor, S. (1998). *Sexual Radiance: A 21-day program of breathwork, nutrition, and exercise for vitality and sensuality.* New York: Harmony Books.

Weed, S. (2002). *New Menopausal Years: The wise woman way.* Woodstock, N.Y.: Ash Tree Pub.

YOGA & MEDITATION

Anderson, S. (2007). *Yoga: Master the basics,* Himalayan Institute Press.

Coulter, H. (2001). *Anatomy of Hatha Yoga: A manual for students, teachers, and practitioners.* Honesdale, PA: Body and Breath.

Frawley, D. (1999). *Yoga and Ayurveda: Self-healing and self-realization.* Twin Lakes, Wis.: Lotus Light Pub.

Iyengar, B. (1979). *Light on Yoga: Yoga dipika.* (rev. [pbk.] edition). New York: Schocken Books.

Kaminoff, L. & Matthews, A. (2011). *Yoga Anatomy.* Champaign, IL: Human Kinetics. (2nd edition).

Long, R. & Macivor, C. (2008). *The Key Poses of Yoga: Your guide to functional anatomy in yoga.* S.l.: Bandha Yoga].

Pandit Rajmani Tigunait (2014). *The Secret of the Yoga Sutras,* Honesdale, PA. Himalayan Institute Press.

Shri Swami Rama (1984). *Exercise Without Movement,* Honesdale, PA. Himalayan Institute Press.

Shri Swami Rama (1982). *Joints and Glands Exercises: As taught by Sri Swami Rama of the Himalayas,* Honesdale, PA. Himalayan International Institute. (2nd edition).

Swami Muktibodhananda Saraswat (1985). *Hatha Yoga Pradipika.* Bihar School of Yoga, Munger, Bihar, India.

HOLISTIC PSYCHOLOGY

Eknath, E. (2010). *Conquest of Mind: Take charge of your thoughts and reshape your life through meditation* (3rd rev. edition). New York. Nilgiri Press.

Eknath, E. (2010). *Patience: A little book of inner strength.* New York. Nilgiri Press.

Harish, Johari (1989). *Breath, Mind, and Consciousness.* Rochester, VT. Destiny Books.

Lama, Dalai (2012). *The Mind's Own Physician: A scientific dialogue with the Dalai Lama on the healing power of meditation.* Oakland, CA. New Harbinger Publications.

Shri Swami Rama (1982). *Creative Use of Emotion,* Honesdale, PA. Himalayan Institute Press.

Shri Swami Rama, Ballentine, R., Swami Ajaya (1976). *Yoga and Psychotherapy: The evolution of consciousness.* Honesdale, PA. Himalayan Institute Press.

Swami Ajaya (1982). *Yoga Psychology: A practical guide to meditation,* Honesdale, PA. Himalayan Institute Press.

Trungpa, C. & Gimian, C. (1984). *Shambhala: The sacred path of the warrior.* Boulder, CO. Shambhala Publications.